# Stuttering Prevented

9

# Stuttering Prevented

WILLIAM H. PERKINS

W

WHURR PUBLISHERS

Singular Publishing Group, Inc.
4284 41st Street
San Diego, California 92105

© **1992 by Singular Publishing Group, Inc.**

**British Library Cataloguing-in-Publication Data**

Perkins, William H.
Stuttering prevented.
I. Title
616.85

ISBN 1-870332-83-0 ✓

*To Jill*

# Contents

Foreword ............................................................. xi

Preface ............................................................. xiii

Who Stutters and Who Doesn't? ........................................... 1

What Is Stuttering? ..................................................... 4

   Short Answers ...................................................... 7

    Why Stutter? ................................................... 7

    Why Become a Stutterer? ......................................... 8

## Section I: Causes

What Causes Stuttering? ................................................ 13

   Why Is Speech Disrupted? .......................................... 14

   Why Try to Speak When We Can't? ................................... 20

   Why Lose Control? ................................................. 23

    Conflict ...................................................... 28

What Causes Stutterers? ............................................... 36

   Stuttering vs. Stutterer .......................................... 36

Stuttering Is Not What It Seems ....................................... 38

Pay-Offs ............................................................................ 42

Explaining the Unexplained ........................................... 44


**Section II: Stuttering Prevented**


Preventing Stuttering ............................................................. 53

Insecurity and Shyness ....................................................... 55

Infancy ............................................................................. 55

Older Childhood .............................................................. 57

How Parents Can Help ..................................................... 59


**Section III: Stuttering Stopped**


What Should Be Stopped and What Shouldn't? ................ 67

Stopping Stuttering ................................................................. 70

Guide to Strategies ........................................................... 71

Who Will Recover Without Help? ..................................... 73

Strategy 1: Help Outgrow Stuttering ............................ 73

Who Will Need Help? ........................................................ 76

Strategy 2: Reduce Excitement Effects ....................... 76

Strategy 3: Reduce Family Pressure Effects .............. 80


**Section IV: Stutterer Prevented**


Stutterer Characteristics ...................................................... 95

Descriptions ..................................................................... 96

Difficulty with Assertiveness ....................................... 96

Attention When Stuttering ............................................97

✳ Insecurity.................................................................98

✳ Self-Image of the Stutterer ......................................99

✳ Shyness ....................................................................100

Frustration or Helplessness ........................................100

Throat, Mouth, or Chest Tightening...........................101

✳ Avoidance and Substitution ......................................102

Has Relative Who Stutters ..........................................103

✳ Hestitant to Speak Out ..............................................105

✳ Unsuccessful in Competition .....................................105

Guide to Strategies ......................................................106

Stutterer Prevention Strategies ..................................108

Strategy 4: Stop Linguistic Stuttering ........................108

Example.....................................................................108

Procedure ..................................................................110

Strategy 5: Stop Assertiveness-Conflict Stuttering ......114

Example.....................................................................114

Procedure ..................................................................116

Strategy 6: Prevent Addictive Pay-Offs .....................120

Example.....................................................................120

General Strategy .......................................................124

Preschool Children ...................................................124

School Children .........................................................126

Stop Stuttering to Prevent Stutterer .........................134

## Section V: Professional Help

Types of Professional Help ..........................................137

Fluency-Management and Counseling Therapies ..........138

Stuttering-Management and Counseling Therapies ........141

Self-Help Groups ................................................................. 147

Psychotherapy .................................................................... 147

Finding Professional Help .................................................. 148

**Section VI: Appendix**

Family Intervention In Stuttering Therapy ...................... 155

# Foreword

There can be no doubt that childhood stuttering presents a clinical equation containing multiple and formidable factors for professionals who provide services for children. The equation involves a child with an emerging developmental concern regarding dysfluency often combined with parental worry magnified by fear of the future and complicated by professionals who are uncertain of how to approach the child or the parent(s). This book offers significant assistance to families and professionals as they assist the child in solving the equation.

Resolving a clinical problem requires a solid understanding of its etiology, common manifestations and potential complications. The fact that the etiology of the majority of dysfluencies is developmental, self-limited, and seldom results in adult stuttering is most often overlooked as the parent focuses on the dreaded label of "stutterer" and magnifies a relatively simple concern into a lifelong problem for the child. Dr. Perkins presents a solid understanding of stuttering's etiology and its common clinical manifestations, but most importantly, he offers advice for the child and parent based on preventing dysfluencies from escalating into stuttering. This approach is itself developmental, and expressed in a manner that can be implemented by parents at any stage of the evolving problem. We are in need of similar approaches to other developmental concerns of childhood.

Alfred Healy, M.D.
Director of Division of Developmental Disorders
University Hospital School
Iowa City, Iowa

# Preface

What I have written here is for parents who may think their child is beginning to stutter. I could not have written it even a year ago. I still had not reached the end of a search which began in the late 1940s. Until I could understand the causes of stuttering, I was not confident that anything said about prevention would be more than sheer conjecture.

From the beginning, the prevailing professional judgment has been that stuttering is unsolvable and incurable. For years this received wisdom from my elders seemed indisputable. Gradually, though, as I learned far more about science by osmosis from a few university colleagues than I ever had by instruction, my confidence grew. With it grew doubts about the infallibility of my professional elders.

Finally, my natural mulishness, stemming no doubt from my Missouri heritage, prevailed. The idea that stuttering could not be solved was too much of a challenge to resist. So I succumbed to that challenge and am satisfied that now, for the most part, it has been met. Whether stuttering can be cured, once it has become a way of life, remains an open question. That it can be prevented, if caught early enough, I have no doubt.

Being recently formulated, the theory of stuttering my colleagues and I have developed will probably be tested by other professionals for years to come. I had a long debate with myself whether or not to wait for completion of all of those tests before writing this guide for parents. I realized that if I had, I doubt that this book would ever be written—at least not in my lifetime. The theory fits all of the known facts about stuttering, so I decided to proceed now because the tests will undoubtedly continue interminably. Since all of the prevention strategies to be offered are helpful under any circumstance, and since the causes we have discovered improve their chances of success, I concluded that waiting to write this would not be in anyone's best interest.

Within my profession I am especially indebted to Raymond Kent, University of Wisconsin, Richard Curlee and Thomas Hixon, University of Arizona, Roger Ingham, University of California, Santa Barbara, and Sulyn Moore, University of South Carolina. Their scientific rigor and extensive knowledge of speech and its physiology have been invaluable as we have labored together to formulate a scientific theory of stuttering for research which became the springboard for the ideas in this book. Without the wise guidance of Robert Blakeley, University of Oregon, this book might never have reached the parents of children who stutter.

Within my University I am particularly grateful to those colleagues who have educated me in the ways of knowing in philosophy, history, medicine, religion, music, art, literature, as well as in the physical, biological, and behavioral sciences. That education spans three decades.

Above all, I am indebted to the guidance of parents who read this book in various stages of preparation. Without them, I would have written it for the only audience I have ever addressed before—my colleagues who have been fed on a rich diet of professional jargon. Without those parents, I would not have discovered that what I have to say can be said in plain English.

Finally, this last decade of my career could not have existed without the superb clinical skills of Debora Sue-O'Brien, and the organizational, editing, writing, and general sanity-inspiring abilities of Christine Sinrud Shade and Christopher Perkins. Their dedication, loyalty, and good cheer have been my anchors.

# Who Stutters and Who Doesn't?

This book is for parents whose children are at risk of stuttering, or who have already started to stutter. Stuttering can have pay-offs. It can become a powerful tool for galvanizing listeners. When it does, the chances of a child's stuttering continuing for life are high. Four-year-old Alex is a case in point. Almost all of the strikes are against him. His parents both have careers. They think fast, talk fast, move fast. As for Alex, he sounds as if he's starting to stutter, so they correct him for that. He also doesn't say his "r" and "s" sounds right, so they correct him for that. To top it off, everyone in the family competes for conversational control. In short, all of these things this family does can contribute heavily to stuttering.

But Alex doesn't stutter, and probably never will. One reason is because his parents are as devoted to him as they are to their careers. Another reason is that there is no history of stuttering, so its tendency to run in families is not a risk. Most important, Alex is a feisty youngster. He is not about to be squelched. He has no trouble controlling a conversation. He announces when he wants into a conversation with "uh, uh, uh, uh," which sounds like

*Whether stuttering can be cured once it has become a way of life, remains an open question. That it can be prevented or stopped if caught early enough I have no doubt.*

1

*If Alex were insecure and his parents only paid attention when he stuttered, this pay-off could easily convert him into a life-long stutterer without his ever knowing why.*

stuttering, but isn't, and then says what he has to say. If he blinked, rolled his eyes, gasped, tightened his throat, and struggled to speak, then his "uh, uh, uhs" probably would be stuttering. He does none of these things.

If Alex were insecure and his parents only paid attention when he stuttered, this pay-off could easily convert him into a life-long stutterer without his ever knowing why. Because Alex is not at all hesitant to assert himself, he will probably never experience the pay-offs of stuttering. That experience occurs to those children who become reluctant to speak out. If they are timid, they are especially vulnerable to fearing assertiveness. Stuttering has pay-offs when listeners stop, pay attention, and are locked in until the disruptions end. Stuttering does for the intimidated speaker what Alex feels free to do openly. Stuttering produces the results of assertiveness without the risk. These pay-offs are not on purpose. The child does not even know they are happening. But their effect in preserving stuttering is very real.

No child is born to stutter. Even if heredity predisposes a child to stutter, it is still not inevitable. It can be prevented. If you suspect that your child stutters, the earlier it is stopped, the better the chances that stuttering will not become chronic. Those chances dwindle as puberty approaches; after high school, they plummet. Once people begin to think of themselves as stutterers, hopes for complete recovery all but vanish. "Once a stutterer, always a stutterer" is the sad lament often heard from adults who stutter.

Far more boys than girls stutter. Not that stuttering is less of a problem for those girls who do, but for every girl there are two to ten times as many boys. One does not have to be male to stutter, but it helps—perhaps because their hormones make them especially vulnerable.

*Stuttering produces the results of assertiveness without the risk.*

What are the odds that your child may stutter? Even more important, if so, what are the odds of recovery? Remarkably, these are difficult questions to answer with certainty. The fact is that experts, as well as laymen, do not agree on what they call stuttering. The result is that estimates vary widely, so the best answers to the questions about odds of stuttering or recovery from it are not very exact.

Still, a ballpark estimate of the probability of a child starting to stutter is about 4 of every 100 children born. Nearly half will recover within a year. About three-fourths will recover by puberty. Only a few more will recover after puberty. As you can see, the best chance of recovery is during childhood. The earlier the better.

This book is about those children who are vulnerable to stuttering, about those who can recover, and even more important, about those who do not recover. Mainly, it is about understanding what can be done to prevent your child from becoming one of the few who are at risk of developing stuttering as a life-long problem.

The recommendations for preventing and stopping stuttering in your child are based on new information. Some of these recommendations can be implemented at home. For others, you may need professional help. The

*No child is born to stutter. Even if heredity predisposes a child to stutter, it is still not inevitable. It can be prevented.*

job can seem so big and challenging as to be overwhelming. Accordingly, the need to keep the tasks to manageable size is paramount.

Bear in mind, no matter what the causes of stuttering, each can be dealt with successfully. There is no mandatory starting point. Improvement of one cause gives momentum to improvement of others. Still, each cause of stuttering has unique features which must be addressed separately.

Stuttering can be prevented during childhood— especially its pay-offs. The key to its prevention is early intervention. The earlier these steps are taken to help, the better the chances for easier communication throughout life. Best of all is to prevent stuttering from birth before it starts.

Many of the strategies that will be mapped out for you in this book take time and effort and a commitment that may be difficult to sustain at times in a busy family life. But the rewards can be enormous. Aside from the benefits to your entire family, the biggest, of course, can be a lifetime of freedom from stuttering for your child.

## What Is Stuttering?

Alex demonstrated what stuttering is and is not. Stuttering is not what you hear. What you hear are disruptions of speech that may sound like stuttering, but unless they feel like stuttering, they are nothing for us to worry about. The only people who know how they feel are the speakers, and the only time they know is when it happens.

What is "it"? Whether with children or adults, "it" is when they lose control of their speech, when they're unable to move ahead, even when they know the word they're trying to say. Once they lose control, these people speak of a feeling of helplessness, of walking to the edge of a cliff, tipping over, and being unable to catch themselves. This is the experience which is troublesome, if not frightening, about stuttering. What you hear when this happens may or may not sound like stuttering. Usually it does, but it need not.

*A ballpark estimate of the probability of a child starting to stutter is about 4 of every 100 children born.*

This is not news for those whose stuttering is a way of life. As Herb Goldberg, President of the Foundation for Fluency, says, "When we stutter *we lose control.*"Jim Laris, Editor of *The Big S*, searched for the word to describe how he feels when he blocks. He had a long list— "angry, scared, bitter, resentful, helpless, humiliated, powerless, small, resigned, hopeless . . . stupid, terrified, paralyzed, crazy, etc." He finally decided that the best description was *powerless.*

Dr. Carl Dell, of Eastern Illinois University, who has devoted his professional life to helping people who stutter, has also spent his own life coping with stuttering. This is what he says happens: "I feel failure at every moment of stuttering, and that's what I'm working on every day in my own life . . . . But that moment when you're absolutely blocked, that moment when you're closed off, that moment when you cannot go forward—I don't think there is anything you can do to stop that moment from happening. That moment is just there. Now, it doesn't happen very long . . . poof, it's gone. But at that moment . . . you're stuck."

These descriptions are from the perspective of the people who stutter. This is how they know that they have stuttered. Incredibly, though, for at least a half century,

*Nearly half will recover within a year. About three-fourths will recover by puberty.*

the people who do the stuttering have had virtually no voice in whether they have stuttered or not when it comes to treatment. The reason is because we professionals have been convinced that we know stuttering when we hear it, so the people who stutter have often been trained to agree with *us* as to when *they* stutter.

It was Dr. Sulyn Moore, at the University of South Carolina, who recently discovered that our professional conviction is dead wrong. What listeners hear carries virtually no information about whether or not the person who stutters *feels* that stuttering has occurred.

This discovery is profoundly important because it means that we have looked at stuttering all of these years through Alice's mirror into Wonderland. We have the problem backwards. What we have heard as stuttering is what we have considered to be the problem. So our prevention strategies and therapies have been designed to deal with the stuttering that we hear. The result has been two clinical approaches: stuttering management and fluency management. With stuttering management, reduction of struggle and fear of stuttering is the objective. With fluency management, establishment and maintenance of stutter-free fluency is the goal.

These are currently the most frequently used approaches. To the extent that reactions to stuttering are part of the problem, as they often are once stuttering becomes chronic, then these approaches can be helpful. Neither approach, however, addresses the causes of stuttering, how to prevent it, or how to stop it.

At this point you have five choices. If you want an overview of this book before diving in more deeply, the ideas are summarized in the outside column. If you want a thumbnail sketch of what causes stuttering and what causes one to become a stutterer (these are very different causes) then you may want to read only the short answers which follow. If you want to know the reasons for these short answers, they are followed by "What Causes Stuttering?" and "What Causes Stutterers?" If you want to turn directly to what you can do to prevent stuttering before it starts, then skip to Section II. If your concern is with stopping stuttering after it has started, then Section III is applicable. If preventing your child from becoming a stutterer is the major issue, then go to Section IV. You can always turn back to Section I for information on causes if you do want to skip ahead now.

*Only a few will recover after puberty. The best chance of recovery is during childhood. The earlier the better.*

## Short Answers

### Why Stutter?

Let's start with what causes stuttering. When we speak, two separate brain operations have to be coordinated. One controls production of the speech sounds with which we form our words. The other controls production of syllables into which the speech sounds must be inserted. If one or the other of these operations is delayed unconsciously, whether for reason of heredity, brain injury, or conflict over assertiveness, then speech will be temporarily disrupted; it will be as if the speaker has been tripped, so speech stumbles for reasons unknown. This

*Aside from the benefits to your entire family, the biggest benefit of early intervention can be a lifetime of freedom from stuttering for your child.*

happens to most everyone from time to time. Most of us don't even notice it has happened, so one does not have to be a stutterer to stutter. In fact, some stutterers who complain most bitterly are rarely heard to stutter. So you see, *being* a stutterer is a very different matter from merely stuttering.

## Why Become A Stutterer?

Why then does one become a stutterer? Whereas understanding why stuttering occurs is a fairly straightforward matter, understanding why one becomes a stutterer is fraught with contradictions. Virtually nothing about it makes logical sense—it isn't what it seems to be. For example, I know of no stutterer who wants to stutter, or who does not feel helpless to prevent it. Yet, all of the evidence says that stuttering has pay-offs and can become addictive. Stutterers want to be free of it, but unconsciously they can't give it up. Why?

The answer I will give you has not been tested in laboratory experiments. It has nothing to do with the popular explanation that stuttering is caused by tightening of the throat. That is merely a description. The *diagnostic* question is: what *causes* the tightening? The answer I will give you is the only one I have been able to find that explains all of the strange contradictions of being a stutterer which I have seen in years of clinical observations. Fortunately, if my answer is wrong no harm will be done, except to my esteem, such as it is. If, however, the answer is correct, then the prospect of being able to prevent children from becoming stutterers is opened. For that matter, the unheard-of prospect of curing stuttering in adults is also opened.

*The discovery process has unfolded over many years . . . . The answers have not come easily.*

After this long preamble, the short answer is this. Children who come to think of themselves as stutterers, and who will build their lives around that image, are insecure in their feelings about being assertive with

*Are you sure about this, Stan? It seems odd that a pointy head and long beak is what makes them fly.*

By permission of Jerry Workman.

*Stuttering is not what you hear. What you hear are disruptions of speech that may sound like stuttering, but unless they feel like stuttering, they are nothing for us to worry about.*

the people to whom they stutter. When this happens their throats or chests tighten, sometimes into a spasm. This is what occurs when they lose control of the speaking situation. The result is that they then lose control of their speech. They stutter. When parents pay little attention to such children except when they stutter, then stuttering becomes a primary tool for gaining attention otherwise unavailable. The fact that such attention is usually negative (parents saying "stop that, slow down," or listeners waiting impatiently for the stuttering to stop so that they can get on with their conversation) does not prevent it from being a pay-off. The worst attention is better than none.

If children knew they were using stuttering for attention, they would not become stutterers. Because these pay-offs are unconscious, stutterers are powerless to prevent their addictive effects. Once children think of themselves as stutterers, this image then protects any fantasies of being powerful. They then become "giants in chains" who cannot expect themselves to be powerful in the real world because they stutter.

# Section I: Causes

*The only people who know how they feel when they stutter are the speakers, and the only time they know is when it happens.*

# What Causes Stuttering?

The basis for what I will say regarding preventing or stopping stuttering from becoming permanent did not emerge full blown like Venus rising from the sea. It grew by bits and pieces. I have long known that prevention of chronic stuttering is possible, that young children have the best chance of recovery. What I have not known until recently is why. The discovery process has unfolded over many years. This long trek has often ended in box canyons that seemed to have no exit. The answers have not come easily.

*Whether with children or adults, stuttering is when they lose control of their speech, when they're unable to move ahead, even when they know the word they're trying to say.*

What has finally emerged is a remarkably clear picture of the nature and causes of stuttering. Surprisingly, the foundation of the explanation is also remarkably simple. So much so in fact that an expert has described it as a scientific version of the old folk wisdom that "stuttering is talking faster than you can think."

The strategies for preventing and stopping stuttering are not mere arbitrary figments of my imagination. Just as medical treatment derives directly from the diagnosis of a problem, recommendations for stopping stuttering also

*Stutterers speak of a feeling of helplessness, of walking to the edge of a cliff, tipping over, and being unable to catch themselves. This is the experience which is troublesome, if not frightening, about stuttering.*

stem directly from the understanding on which they are based.

What do we have to know about stuttering to stop it? The list is remarkably short:

1. Why is speech disrupted?
2. Why does one feel compelled to speak when disrupted?
3. Why does one feel helpless to speak when one's control is lost?

### Why Is Speech Disrupted?

Speech happens so automatically and easily that it seems to be all one piece. This impression is bolstered by how rapidly we talk. At a comfortable rate, we utter about 14 sounds per second. That's twice as fast as we can control our tongue, lips, jaw or any other parts of our speech mechanism when we move them separately. But put them all together for speech and they work the way fingers of expert typists and concert pianists do. Their movements overlap in a symphony of exquisite timing.

The possibility that movements of such speed and precision, involving the coordination of about 100 speech muscles, could be the product of a vast assembly of countless neural (nerve) "decisions" seems all but unbelievable, but that is the truth of the matter. The trail of these decisions is relatively long, but taking a short cut will still lead ultimately and directly to the explanation of stuttering.

A simplistic analogy of an automobile assembly line may help you to understand how speech is assembled. The answer to stuttering lies in the timing of this assembly. Probably no one will be much enlightened to be told that the final assembly of a car involves two major components: the body and the engine. The body consists of the chassis, wheels, and transmission; the engine consists of the cylinder block in which the pistons and valves operate in conjunction with a fuel system and an electrical system.

Similarly, the final assembly of speech involves two major components: speech sounds and syllables. Speech sounds are what alphabet letters represent when words are spelled. Syllables contain the speech sounds.

Syllables have a vital function essential to stuttering: tone of voice. Tone of voice tells nothing about the words we speak, but it tells volumes about us, whether we're happy or depressed, how we feel about what we're saying, how we feel about who we're saying it to. Tone of voice is what tells me the kind of evening it's going to be when I come home and say, "Hi," and my wife replies "Hi." The words don't vary, but the tone-of-voice *message* can range from glorious to dismal.

Tone of voice has a very ancient history. It's the human equivalent of a dog's whine, a cat's meow, a lion's roar, a bird's song. And we use tone of voice for essentially the same reason, to announce how we feel about what's important to us. Ironically, this is the part of speech of which we are hardly aware, and yet we react to it as if it tells us the truth about what's being said,

*Children who come to think of themselves as stutterers, and who will build their lives around that image, are insecure in their feelings about being assertive with the people to whom they stutter.*

*Why stuttering occurs has nothing to do with the popular explanation that it is caused by tightening of the throat. That is merely a description. The* **diagnostic question is: what** **causes** *the* **tightening?**

whether it's sarcastic, devious, or sincere. In essence, we react to it as if it were the foundation of what is being said—which it is.

Our ability to express ideas in words is the new kid on the evolutionary block. We didn't acquire this ability until about 100,000 years ago. When we did learn to talk, we built this extraordinary ability on the foundation of tone of voice, the vocal signal system we inherited from millions and millions of years of animal communication.

What this adds up to for speech is the need to assemble our new language system into our ancient tone of voice system every time we express ourselves in words. For the most part, our ideas are carried by the speech sounds which form the words. By contrast, tone of voice is carried exclusively in the syllables. We cannot speak until these two components are assembled, any more than a car without its engine can be driven.

## HAGAR THE HORRIBLE by Dik Browne

Reprinted with special permission of King Features Syndicate, Inc.

Let's return to the auto assembly line analogy. Cars, of course, are made of thousands of parts which, in turn, are made of raw materials from all over the world. The parts themselves can also be built anywhere in the world. These parts are then assembled into larger units— wheels, doors, chassis, transmissions, engine assemblies, and the like. Final assembly brings all of the larger units together along two assembly lines, one for the body and one for the engine.

By the same token, speech is made of millions of parts —probably billions. Their raw materials, neurons, come from all over the brain. The neural equivalent of parts can also be "built" anywhere in the brain. These parts are then assembled into larger brain units which will ultimately be used in two "assembly lines," one for speech sounds and one for syllables. (I cannot resist the temptation to point out that those who claim to have discovered the cause of stuttering in the brain are premature, to say the least. We are just beginning to discover the functions the brain has to perform for stuttering, let alone know the locations in the brain where these functions occur.)

The crux of stuttering is now at hand. Back at the assembly line, if the auto body arrives ready to have the engine inserted, but the assembly of the engine has been delayed, then the body, which has wheels, can be pushed off the assembly line, but it cannot be driven off. It is not yet a finished car.

For speech, this would be equivalent to having the syllable ready for final assembly, but the speech sounds

*When stutterers speak, their throats or chests tighten, sometimes into a spasm. This is what occurs when they lose control of the speaking situation. The result is that they then lose control of their speech. They stutter.*

*What do we have to know about stuttering to stop it? The list is remarkably short:*

*1. Why is speech disrupted?*

*2. Why does one feel compelled to speak when disrupted?*

*3. Why does one feel helpless to speak when one's control is lost?*

intended for insertion into that syllable are delayed. Anytime a vocal sound is made it's a syllable—a laugh, a burp, a groan, a meow, a bark, a chirp—all are syllables even though they are not speech. When the sounds are ready for integration, that is when we know what we want to say. So if we have syllables ready for production, but the speech sounds aren't ready, we can say things like "uh-uh," "er-er," or even words can be spoken, but they will not be part of the idea we're trying to express. We would still be helplessly stuck. This would be the basis for what could be called *linguistic stuttering*, which probably predominates among children. As long as it does not carry pay-offs, it will probably be outgrown.

Now let's suppose that the reverse assembly disruption happens. On the car assembly line, the engine would arrive with no body to put it in. Without a body with wheels, it couldn't go anywhere or do anything. It would just have to sit there until its body arrived.

On the speech assembly line, the speech sounds would arrive telling us that we know the word we want to say. But, the syllable for those sounds would not have arrived, so we would be involuntarily blocked from continuing with any sound, with no idea why. Without the syllables into which speech sounds insert, words cannot be uttered. This is what could be called *self-expressive stuttering*, because it would result when self-expressive tone of voice is delayed in being integrated into the syllable. This is the type of stuttering which seems to predominate when the problem becomes chronic, and is most likely to have addictive pay-off effects which lead to becoming a stutterer.

Thus, speech can be disrupted because the brain has processed sounds more slowly than syllables, or syllables more slowly than sounds. If sounds are delayed in children, it is usually because of linguistic uncertainty (the child can't think of the word wanted or of how to phrase what to say). We have to know the words that are arranged in phrases before our brains can automatically process the sounds that are needed. If sounds are delayed, we know that we haven't yet figured out what we want to say. We're not always aware of our linguistic uncertainties, but anytime we choose to think about them, we can. Which is to say that the typical reason for delayed sound processing, linguistic uncertainty, is potentially available to awareness.

*Syllables have a vital function essential to stuttering: tone of voice.*

Most of the causes of delayed syllable processing are very different from the causes of delayed sound processing. When we speak automatically, the cause, whether heredity, brain injury, or conflict, could have the same effect: the efficiency of neural resources the brain needs to process syllables could be reduced. The result would

**MARVIN** by Tom Armstrong

Reprinted with special permission of North America Sydicate, Inc.

*The final assembly of speech involves two major components: speech sounds and syllables. Speech sounds are what alphabet letters represent when words are spelled. Syllables contain the speech sounds.*

be to retard the rate at which we could produce syllables. This would leave us knowing the word we want to say (the sounds would have arrived ready for integration), but with no knowledge that the reason we can't say it is because the syllable for those sounds has not arrived.

There is no known treatment for two of these causes, heredity and brain injury. At least not yet. Fortunately, they are probably not the primary causes of most stuttering that becomes permanent. Admittedly, they can cause severe speech disruptions if you talk fast enough, but they do not explain easily why the disruptions vary from situation to situation and person to person.

The third, and most likely cause, is a dominance conflict about being assertive—about being in control. One's "peck-order" position exists in every social interaction, and it can change swiftly from moment to moment. We can be dominating a discussion, for instance, only to have someone else enter the conversation and take control of it for the evening. If we resent the intrusion and try to reenter the conversation while feeling the intruder has stolen our power, we will be uneasy about feeling free to speak out. This is the conflict which can delay syllable processing, with its consequent disruptions, and which can vary from situation to situation and person to person.

## Why Try to Speak When We Can't?

Why try to stumble ahead with speech when the words won't come out? After all, we could just stop and wait for syllable or sound processing to catch up with each other. We could then proceed fluently. The answer to why those who stutter don't pause takes us in a different direction. Parts of the answer are fairly obvious. Other parts are hidden deeper. The term which best summarizes all of the parts is *time pressure*. We will use it in the broadest sense to include any pressure, whether outside or inside of

*Tone of voice . . . is the human equivalent of a dog's whine . . . we react to it as if it were the foundation of what is being said— which it is.*

By permission of George Booth.

*Speech is made of millions of parts— probably billions. These raw materials, neurons, come from all over the brain. The neural equivalent of assembled parts can also be "built" anywhere in the brain.*

speakers, to continue talking when disrupted or to speed up their speaking rate.

We will begin with an obvious source of pressure, the listener's expectation for us to hurry up and finish what we're saying. It can be in the form of explicit command, "hurry up!" Or it can be implicit; people hovering restlessly waiting to butt into our conversation. A frequently occurring form, which stutterers remember bitterly from childhood, is to be raised in a family of competitive talkers. Talking in these families is like driving the Los Angeles freeways—everyone cuts in on everyone else. Anyone who doesn't, doesn't get into the conversation.

Then there are some relatively obvious internal pressures, such as talking when excited, or angry, or serious. Or frustrated. Dr. Oliver Bloodstein of Brooklyn College has a major theory of stuttering that is built around the frustration of children who struggle to learn to talk. This theory proposes that speech is disrupted by the tensions and fragmentations of their struggles to speak.

A far more universal pressure is not so obvious. It is reflexive time pressure. When speaking automatically and fluently, the syllables flow trippingly off the tongue. There is no expectation that the flow will not continue. Dr. Richard Curlee, at the University of Arizona, likens it to walking through a series of swinging doors. As we get to each we expect it to open easily, but if it sticks a bit, we will automatically push on it. If it sticks more, we will push harder. The reaction is so automatic it is almost reflexive.

Imagine these swinging doors as syllables in words. Here is the basis for a universal form of time pressure—it is the picture of what happens in stuttering. If a syllable sticks a bit when we push on it slightly, the result is a repetition. If it sticks more, we push harder and the slow easy repetition becomes faster and harder. If it sticks even harder, the repetitions turn into solid blocks.

The troubling part of this answer, as far as it goes, is that everyone experiences these time pressures one way or another. Why aren't we all stuttering? Are some people more vulnerable than others? This question leads us into deeper water.

*Neural parts are assembled into larger brain units which will ultimately be used in two "assembly lines," one for speech sounds and one for syllables.*

## Why Lose Control?

If you didn't know how to escape an involuntary speech disruption and were under time pressure, then you would know why a speaker loses control. Unlike Alex, who not only doesn't stutter but also has no relatives who ever did, Sue, a child who does stutter, has a mother and grandmother who both stuttered. Little wonder, then, that she began to stutter as soon as she started trying to express herself in speech when she was about two years old. Girls don't stutter as a rule, but when they do, heredity may be suspected. If stuttering is on the mother's side of the family, odds are much higher that it will be inherited than if it's on the father's side. So far, Sue is an only child, but if she were to have a brother, chances of his stuttering would be much higher than for a sister; boys are

*Syllables cannot be spoken without a vocal component which expresses how we feel.*

far more apt to inherit vulnerability to stutter than girls, especially when inherited from the mother. Heredity can limit how fast one can speak without losing control, so when Sue is exuberant her speech is bound to be disrupted involuntarily.

What is particularly intriguing about Sue is that she's a warm, confident, happy little girl, until she speeds up when trying to talk. Any time she gets excited, she stutters. Even when playing alone with her dolls, if she talks fast while scolding one of them, she stutters. Naturally, she is frustrated when it happens. It is even more disturbing for her when she tries to break into a conversation. This inevitably triggers stuttering. So far, she is living with this problem about as gracefully as could be expected. Because Sue's stuttering shows major signs of being hereditary, she will probably not outgrow it. Her best hope is to learn to talk slower than the speed at which stuttering

**MARVIN** by Tom Armstrong

Reprinted with special permission of North American Syndicate, Inc.

is triggered. Fortunately, she is showing indications of figuring this out on her own. She now holds up her hand for attention before she tries to enter a conversation.

The difference between Alex and Sue holds the key to why people who stutter lose control. Although Alex is frequently under time pressure, he does not feel helpless when he does what sounds like stuttering. When Sue stutters, however, it comes out of nowhere; it just reaches out and grabs her unexpectedly when she talks too fast.

To understand loss of control (stuttering) requires understanding the two basic conditions which are necessary. One involves disruption of speech for reasons of which the speaker is relatively unaware and unable to prevent. As we have seen, syllables consist mainly of vocal characteristics which provide little if any information about words to be spoken. If the brain's preparation of syllables were delayed, speakers would not know why their speech was mysteriously disrupted. Heredity, or certain types of brain injury, could produce this result. But the effects would tend to be relatively permanent. Every time speakers talked faster than their neural limits to produce syllables, their speech would be disrupted. This is what happens to Sue. It can, but need not, have addictive pay-offs. More typically, stuttering varies from moment to moment, from speaking situation to speaking situation. A cause of disruption is needed to account for such variations. As we will soon see, a dominance conflict, the most likely basis for pay-offs, meets that need.

*Speech can be disrupted because the brain has processed sounds more slowly than syllables, or syllables more slowly than sounds.*

*If sounds are delayed in children, it is usually because of linguistic uncertainty (the child can't think of the word wanted or of how to phrase what to say).*

The other basic reason for loss of control involves time pressure to continue talking once disrupted. Take Billy, for example. When he was four and becoming increasingly active, his older brother, Henry, began a campaign to dominate him. One of the first things that Henry did was to butt into a conversation every time Billy tried to talk. This didn't stop Billy from trying, but it put him under considerable pressure to get into the conversation in the first place. And it kept him under pressure to keep control of it even when he didn't know what he was going to say next.

The more urgent the time pressure the greater the loss of control. The reason is obvious. When our speech is disrupted we cannot proceed with what we're trying to say. But if, nonetheless, we try to proceed while we cannot, we won't succeed. We will have lost control of our ability to continue with what we want to say. The harder we push, the faster we will be trying to talk. The gap will become bigger between the rate at which we're trying to speak and the rate at which the brain can get syllables and sounds integrated so that we *can* speak. It is the requirement of time pressure which offers the most potential for preventing stuttering from starting, or from stopping it in children once it starts.

What all of this adds up to are two things which determine loss of control: unawareness of cause of disruption, and time pressure. With normal time pressure, one could be relatively unaware of disruptions and be able to push through them automatically. They would feel like natural disruptions rather than stuttering.

Similarly, to the extent one is aware of cause of disruption, such as linguistic uncertainty, high time pressure still would not produce stuttering. If one knows why the disruption, then one knows what can be done to correct it, so it is not experienced as loss of control, hence as stuttering. The problem with knowing why is that the causes most apt to produce life-long stuttering—conflict and heredity— are not available to awareness. Commenting on the difficulty, if not impossibility, of controlling stuttering, Steve Loynachen, writing in *Letting Go*, a publication of the National Stuttering Project, said, "I find it hard to believe that you can control something that you hate, no matter how hard you work at it."

*Most of the causes of delayed syllable processing are very different from the causes of delayed sound processing.*

Within the range of these extreme conditions are the trade-offs between awareness and time pressure. When time pressure is low, we can be relatively unaware of the cause of disruption and still not feel as if we have stuttered. On the other hand, when vaguely aware of the cause of disruption, time pressure can be moderately severe before the feeling of losing control begins.

It is a dominance conflict, though, which puts one in double jeopardy. On one hand, it disrupts speech for reasons one cannot understand. This is a major cause of losing control and feeling helpless. At the same time, it puts one under time pressure. As we have seen, time pressure has many causes—excitement, anger, dispute, persuasion, and the like. Alone, they impel one to control the conversation, and possibly to speak louder, higher, and faster. None of these causes alone, however, are likely to result in speech disruptions. Without disruption, no basis ex-

*The relative status of who we talk to has a bearing on what we talk about, even more on how we phrase what we say, and most of all on our tone of voice.*

ists for loss of control or helplessness. The only condition which produces both disruption and time pressure simultaneously is a dominance conflict. Whatever the causes, when one is in double jeopardy of being both disrupted involuntarily and put under time pressure, the result is predictable: stuttering. Add to this the addictive potential of conflict-driven stuttering and the predictable result becomes chronic stuttering. This conflict is so important to becoming a stutterer that we will consider it at greater length.

## Conflict

For severe stuttering, the most powerful source of time pressure is also a powerful source of speech disruption. Conflict. But not just any conflict. What we need to consider is a conflict that can occur, potentially, in any speaking situation. Paradoxically, the conflict we seek, to explain why only some stutter, is not unique to people who stutter; it is found in all animals that live in socially organized groups.

In lower animals, survival of the species is achieved by survival of the fittest. Before breeding season, males, in particular, fight for breeding rights. Between seasons, however, peace is generally preserved by each animal accepting its position in a dominance hierarchy. They do this with signals, including vocal signals, which are an important part of animal communication systems. It is this vocal signal system that is a foundation of our spoken language.

With the advent of civilization, man has tried to move away from the principle of survival of the fittest.

Democratic societies at least declare that they extol equal rights and opportunities for all. And yet dominance hierarchies prevail in every nook and cranny of human interaction. Some of these hierarchies are formalized, such as in business organizations and the military. Some exist implicitly, as in doctor/patient relations. These hierarchies are not universal, however. They exist only when you are involved in them. The hierarchy from which no one can escape is personal.

The dominance hierarchy in which we all live and interact is expressed in the old saw, "all men are created equal, but some are more equal than others."  I have searched in vain for a human interaction in which dominance is not a fundamental issue in how one speaks. The relative status of who we talk to has a bearing on what we talk about, even more on how we phrase what we say, and most of all on our tone of voice.

Normally, we think of stuttering increasing when speaking to persons of authority. But for Ben, a young bank executive, the reverse situation seemed to be at work. He spoke fluently with his president, yet stuttered severely with bank secretaries and clerks. With his president, an elderly man of distinction, the status gap seemed so great that he didn't expect to even be noticed—any recognition was appreciated. Ben's staff, however, was another matter. He felt vastly superior to them, so such respect and deference as they accorded seemed grossly insufficient to him. Yet, he felt that to protest would demean himself unbearably. Only after many hours of psychotherapy did he discover why he had no problem speaking to his boss, but was continually blocked when talking to any of his staff.

*When we speak automatically, heredity, brain injury, or conflict could have the same effect: the efficiency of neural resources the brain needs to process syllables could be reduced.*

*Heredity and brain injury are probably not the primary causes of most stuttering that becomes permanent.*

As long as we are comfortable with our status, no conflict about dominance exists. A dominance conflict depends on expectations of assertiveness, of the ability to control a speaking situation, whether our status be dominant or subordinate. But when we feel that our listener accords us less respect than we feel we deserve, yet do not feel free to protest, then a dominance conflict sets in which can contribute mightily to stuttering. It fuels time pressure by depriving us of feeling the right to speak out, so that when we do enter a conversation it is as if we have to push our way in. This speeds up how fast we talk.

At the same time, a dominance conflict delays the rates at which our brains can formulate syllables. Syllables, remember, cannot be spoken without a vocal-signal component which expresses how we feel. If we feel slighted, but are in conflict over the tone of voice to use in protest, then delayed syllable processing will result. It can disrupt our speech for reasons we will not know. What will also result is a tightening of throat, mouth, or chest, which may be the basic cause of the disruption. We will have to slow down during the conflict if our speech is not to be disrupted. But conflict drives time pressure, instead, to speed up our rate. So the effect of conflict is a triple whammy—it retards how fast we can integrate syllables and sounds, while at the same time speeding up how fast we actually have to integrate them, and then tightens throat, mouth, or chest. Severe stuttering is made from this combination.

Effects of a dominance conflict go even farther. Without it, there would be no need for the pay-offs of stuttering. When one can be easily assertive, can easily control a conversation, the attention stuttering provides is not needed. Similarly, power fantasies are not needed. Without these pay-offs, the addictiveness of stuttering dwindles to insignificance. A dominance conflict provides the typical soil in which chronic stuttering grows. Now is as good a time as any to see where this growth often leads. In the process, evidence of the addictive quality of stuttering will be seen.

John was a case in point. He was one of eight men who, years ago, volunteered for what they thought was a learning experiment. None knew that they were selected because of their severe stuttering. Actually, their stuttering varied depending on who they talked with, a sure sign that a major cause of their stuttering was conflict.

John was teamed with an attractive and friendly girl, whom he did not know was really part of the research team. He was mustering up his courage to ask for a date when the experiment began. He was told the effects of two types of punishment, the word "no" and different levels of electric shock, were being tested on accuracy of impressions of a person's tastes. Today, federal disclosure regulations would prohibit the experiment.

It was prearranged that the girl drew the straw for writing her impressions of John, and he drew the straw to administer punishment if her impressions were wrong.

While John was being hooked up to a bank of equipment that measured blood pressure, heart rate, and breathing, he was allowed to "inadvertently" overhear a phony story that the girl's written impressions were

*The most likely cause of stuttering is a dominance conflict about being assertive— about being in control.*

*Dominance conflict about being assertive can delay syllable processing, with its consequent disruptions, and can vary from situation to situation and person to person.*

insulting and demeaned his masculinity. Needless to say, John felt betrayed—the girl had seemed so nice.

The experiment proceeded. John was given a brief sample of the levels of intensity of shock he could administer. The higher levels were severe jolts—real hair straighteners—which he could barely endure, even briefly.

The girl was attached to the shock unit and related her 20 impressions of his tastes. If he agreed with her impression, no shock was to be given. The more he disagreed the higher the shock should be. But despite her apparent efforts to judge his tastes accurately, John gave her prolonged maximum shock for all 20 impressions. She gritted her teeth, her eyes rolled up in her head and she appeared on the verge of passing out before it was over.

In reality, no shock was ever administered. The girl was able to discreetly turn off the shock with a switch under the table and then simulated a reaction appropriate to the level of shock John thought he gave.

The actual purpose of the experiment was to determine the relationships among stuttering, anger, and retaliation. When John was later told the true purpose, he was less than pleased to learn he had been deceived, but showed little remorse for administering what he thought at the time was severe shock.

John, and all the other subjects, were gentle men, not given to visible aggression or anger. Yet the other three who used shock also did as John did—they gave the girl who betrayed them what they thought were 20 maximum doses.

Most of the results were expected: stuttering increased when these men were made angry, and it was sharply reduced when they could retaliate with shock, which they used with vengeance. The four men who could only signal disagreement by saying "no" had no reduction in their stuttering. Instead, it increased dramatically. Their fury appeared to be unrelieved. When the physiological measures were analyzed, those measures that were elevated by anger were also reduced by retaliating with shock. Again, this was expected.

But there was a surprising, unexpected, result. The four men whose stuttering increased in severity, because they could only say "no," had a much greater blood pressure reduction than did the four who retaliated with open fury approved by experimental sanction. The four who could only say "no" apparently found more relief from their anger by stuttering severely than by using shock. This unexpected result was confirmed in a subsequent experiment which we will visit later. I am convinced it has extraordinary implications.

This tale illustrates that much goes on below the surface of conflict-driven stuttering. But why should we be concerned with men for whom stuttering is a way of life? After all, we're interested in preventing or stopping stuttering in children. But this is exactly why stuttering in these adults is of concern. They started stuttering as children. The seeds of what they became were sown when they were very young.

John had been a timid little boy. He said in later years that though his mother *had told* him how much she loved him, he never believed her because she didn't *act* as if she loved him. He felt that his brothers and sisters were always favored, that his family listened to them, but he

*Why try to stumble ahead with speech when the words won't come out? After all, we could just stop and wait for syllable or sound processing to catch up with each other. We could then proceed fluently.*

*Imagine swinging doors as syllables in words. Here is the basis for a universal form of time pressure—it is the picture of what happens in stuttering.*

couldn't get a word in edgewise. He tried to tell his mother how hurt and angry he was—that he thought her actions showed how little she cared for him. He resented her for undercutting his attempts to tell her all she gave him were words he couldn't believe, words which protected her from his protests.

John's story has a sequel. Four months after the experiment, he awakened one morning, talked aloud to himself to prove, as usual, that he could speak normally, at least when alone. He felt no different than ever—until he had to use the phone, an infernal contraption he hated and feared. His stuttering was severe, except with a few close friends. With the phone, speech was sheer torture. On this morning, he dialed the number with trembling expectation of the worst. When he heard his boss answer (the signal for his speech to freeze solid) what came out of his mouth was a fast flow of fluent speech. His stutter was gone.

John was more shocked than his boss. He had no idea why this had happened. It was a miracle he was only too happy to enjoy while it lasted. For the first time he could remember, he spoke as freely and easily as he had always dreamed of doing.

Then reality set in. He knew it wouldn't last, so he called everyone with whom he had stuttered most. He was certain that by evening he would be, as he said, "stuttering up a storm" again. Evening came and he was still fluent. He awakened next morning braced for a faded miracle. But the miracle didn't fade. Now he began to wonder if he *could* stutter, so he tried time after time throughout the day, with no success. The possibility began to dawn on him that he might never stutter again. That thought almost paralyzed him. How was he going to cope if he couldn't stutter?  Waves of anxiety washed through him. By the next night he said he felt as if he were being skinned alive on a platform in a public square.

John endured a month of endless panic. By the time the panic ended he had gone through a complete reversal of personality. Whereas before he had been gentle and soft spoken to the point of shyness—he was barely able to squeeze a word out—what emerged was an openly angry man who snarled at the slightest provocation. But he snarled fluently. Gradually, his belligerence gave way to a more socially palatable aggressiveness. To this day he remains free of stuttering, one of the few "cures" I have ever  known.

In John's case, the proverbial ounce of prevention would have been stopping his stuttering in childhood. Had it been stopped, he would not have had to pay such a gigantic price for his vastly improbable cure.

Some people, such as John, are probably more vulnerable to a dominance conflict than others. For instance, if we are naturally shy or timid (people are born with many of the temperaments they will have for life), then we are more likely to have difficulty being  assertive. It does not mean we can't be; it means our natural tendency is to shy away from assertive situations. It also means that people will tend to take advantage of us, which increases the likelihood of our being in conflict over not being assertive.

*If a syllable sticks a bit when we push on it slightly, the result is a repetition. If it sticks more, we push harder and the slow easy repetition becomes faster and harder. If it sticks even harder, the repetitions turn into solid blocks.*

*To understand loss of control (stuttering) requires understanding the two basic conditions which are necessary.*

Being born shy does not mean that we are born insecure. Security depends more on the type of parenting received in the early years. Secure timid people are less likely to be caught up in dominance conflicts than are those born assertive who become insecure. Studies have shown that parents who respond to their babies' needs when they reach out to be held, or when they cry, tend to produce secure children. Insecure children are produced by parents who tend to ignore what their children want. They may pick them up and play with them as much as parents of secure children, but they do it when *they* want to do it, not when their *children* want it done. This was John's complaint exactly.

# What Causes Stutterers?

## Stuttering vs. Stutterer

Implicit in the foregoing analysis of a dominance conflict is the wide chasm between *stuttering* and being a *stutterer*. Everyone loses control of their speech from time to time, so that means that everyone stutters to one extent or another. For most, stuttering doesn't occur very often, and when it does, it is eventually outgrown, especially in childhood. Becoming a stutterer is quite another matter. It is those who join this group for whom the adage, "once a stutterer always a stutterer," applies.

People can even stutter chronically, say for hereditary reasons, and still not think of themselves as stutterers. One of the things those who call themselves stutterers have in common is that stuttering is such a problem that they build their lives around it. Some are never even heard to stutter, yet frequently complain more bitterly about it than those who stutter severely. They apparently know they are at risk of stuttering for the same reason those who stutter openly know—their throats, mouths, or chests tighten. Stuttering is just below the surface. As described by Dr. Walter Manning, a professor at Memphis State University who also stutters, one speaks "the way one would walk across the slippery stones of a mountain stream or across the thin ice on a lake. You may or may not slip or break through the ice. You have not fallen yet. But . . . you may lose your balance, your control." The difference between those who stutter openly and those who don't is that one group hides their stuttering by suppressing loss of control. The other group succumbs and loses control. Ironically, this group, whose members may stutter severely, seems less disturbed by it than those who hide their stuttering.

*One cause of stuttering involves disruption of speech for reasons of which the speaker is relatively unaware and unable to prevent.*

Why do 20 to 30 percent of children who stutter become stutterers while the vast majority either outgrow it or are not bothered by it? The answer is that those who do not outgrow it discover addictive pay-offs which turn stuttering into a powerful tool for coping with assertiveness. Even when stuttering in children is fueled by heredity or brain injury, these pay-offs are available only when their stuttering is caused, at least in part, by a dominance conflict.

Although children live in a world of fantasies which can be fed by such conflicts, protection of these fantasies

*The other basic reason for loss of control involves time pressure to continue talking once disrupted.*

with stuttering does not become a pay-off until children who stutter become stutterers. That troublesome self-concept emerges when they become addicted to using stuttering to gain the rewards of assertiveness without the risk of doing it openly. Once established, the stuttering becomes a protective pay-off for the fantasy images associated with being a stutterer.

I realize that with this assertion I am crawling out on a limb which may break off behind me. But I doubt it. In my early clinical days I used psychotherapy. I spent 12 years listening for thousands of hours with my "third ear" to people who stuttered. Yet I have always had a gnawing suspicion that I was missing something that they were trying to tell me. They didn't know what it was any more than I did. Now, I think I know.

My confidence that the limb I'm crawling out on is strong is bolstered by a letter I received from one of the finest therapists I know. Elizabeth Versteegh has also listened for thousands of hours in Holland to hundreds of people of all ages who stutter. We have used very different therapies, and yet, unbeknownst to either of us, I discovered from her letter that we have reached virtually identical conclusions about the nature of stuttering. If our ideas are right, addictiveness is at the root of becoming a stutterer. To prevent this identity would require nipping the bud of this addictiveness in childhood before it takes root.

## Stuttering Is Not What It Seems

Let's start by putting together some of the strange things about stuttering which don't seem to make sense.

We'll begin with John and the experiment. Why did stuttering reduce physical signs of anger more than use of what John and the others thought was severe shock? John was furious and his use of shock, which was sanctioned by the experiment, gave him a golden opportunity to vent his wrath without inhibition. Which he did. And so did the other three men who used shock. It relieved their stuttering and it relieved physical evidence of their anger.

What doesn't make sense is the lowered blood pressure response of the other four men, who could only say "no." Why was their apparent reduction of anger so much greater when the only thing which could account for it was their sharply increased stuttering? Saying "no" hardly gave them satisfactory retaliation. Even more puzzling is how stuttering, which they feared, could be so apparently rewarding? It could have been a fluke in the experiment, but when the essence of it was repeated in another experiment, the same result happened without exception in 16 men who stuttered.

Then there is what stutterers say when they describe what it is like to stutter. The late Dr. Joseph Sheehan of the University of California, Los Angeles, who himself stuttered, and was seen by others who stuttered as their spokesman, was forceful in his description of the guilt and shame of stuttering. More recently, Dr. Carl Dell, of whom we have already spoken, speaks to the same point. "It is baloney to feel failure every time you stutter. That is just crazy. It is not your fault . . . . The very moment the stuttering first happens to you, I don't think there is anything you can do about it." Then, later, he says, "If this sense of failure [when I stutter] is my worst feeling . . . ,

*The more urgent the time pressure the greater the loss of control.*

***What all of this adds up to are two things which determine loss of control: unawareness of cause of disruption and time pressure.***

the second worst is when I fail to say something I want to say, or fail to talk to a person I want to talk to, or fail to introduce myself."

What is strangest about these statements to begin with is that the feeling about stuttering doesn't jibe with the causes of feeling guilt, shame, or failure. These feelings go with responsibility. If you do something harmful you could have prevented, such as running into someone while driving when drunk, then guilt, shame, and failure are predictable. But if you injured someone because another car caused an accident you couldn't prevent, regret would make sense, but not guilt, shame, or failure. So as Dell says, "It is baloney to feel failure every time you stutter . . . . It is not your fault."  And yet, failure is what he says he feels every time he stutters.

*"I don't recall any speaker displaying such contempt for the intelligence of an audience."*

By permission of Bardulf Ueland. Cartoon from *Science.*

But if he feels this way about stuttering, then *not* stuttering should relieve his feeling of failure. To the contrary, avoiding occasions to stutter are, he says, almost as big a cause to feel failure.

Then there are the strange conditions under which stuttering does not occur. Larry Stein, a self-described stutterer, said, "Ironically, the best period of speech in my entire life was when I was terribly depressed. I had given up on life and I felt pain, I felt anguish, I felt helplessness . . . . I was no longer competing with anyone, including the older members of my family. I had just totally given up."

Hardly a description, this statement, of how one would expect a person who stutters to feel when freest of stuttering. It's even more puzzling when paired with another's statement, in *Letting Go*. "When I find myself stuttering, my most effective solution has not been trying for greater fluency; such efforts, for me, invariably seem to result in more stuttering. The most effective intervention for me  has been to examine the interactive situation I happen to be in . . . and then, try to resolve that discomfort . . . to put me more in a state dominated by *approach* [assertiveness] . . . ."

These are diametrically opposite statements. One extols the virtue (if you can call it that) of total submissiveness, the other of dominance, in freeing these two people from their stuttering. How can this be?  Is there some common link which frees them?

Finally, the strangest part of all was John's overnight transformation. Before the transformation, he was one whose stuttering was terribly severe and who personally

*It is the requirement of time pressure which offers the most potential for preventing stuttering from starting, or from stopping it in children once it starts.*

*The only condition which produces both disruption and time pressure simultaneously is a dominance conflict.*

was the gentlest of men. After, he was completely fluent and uninhibitedly aggressive. Why did such a wildly improbable change occur? What could have happened? No one knew, least of all John.

### Pay-Offs

Now let's reconstruct what seems to have happened yo John by drawing on the strangenesses just recounted. What if, in the early development of stuttering, children begin to experience their stuttering as a safe method of assertion? They don't stutter on purpose. They don't even know they're getting any pay-off. It just happens. Early on, the pay-offs could be the parents' concern, sometimes bordering on panic. Later, it could be the control it gives the child. For instance, stuttering makes some listeners uncomfortable; they don't know how to react. They are apt to be held in limbo until the stuttering stops. If they do try to help by finishing a blocked word or phrase, for example, or butt into the middle of a block, nothing makes a person who stutters angrier—which makes sense once stuttering becomes a hidden method of assertion. How would you feel if you were trying to stand up to someone and they patted you on the head and helped you to be angry? What could be more demeaning!

An even deeper pay-off is in the power of stuttering to preserve "giant-in-chains" fantasies that are widely recognized among people who stutter. For instance, I heard statements such as this frequently during the years I used psychotherapy for treatment: "When I look at my thoughts inside, they're white and important, but when I speak them they change color to black and they seem to be degraded and foolish. It's like I'm constantly painting masterpieces. Of course I know they aren't real masterpieces, but they feel like it inside, and the only way I can protect them is to spoil them so people won't know for sure that they weren't masterpieces. You know, I just realized that that's what I do to my speech and my ideas when I stutter." An example of another recurring theme was this: "Once I start talking I just can't stop. I love words. They're the most powerful, beautiful things I know." This was spoken by a person who stuttered severely.

All of these "strangenesses" seem to boil down to three things: fantasies of power, with speech as a tool for achieving that power; stuttering as the method of protecting a powerful self-image; and stuttering as an effective method of being in control without being openly assertive, aggressive, or angry. These all seem to fit the results of the experiment in which John retaliated with shock. In fact, that experiment speaks to how powerful stuttering (and its fantasies) seem to be. Stuttering was apparently stronger than severe shock as a method of assertion and retaliation.

If all this seems to be an unbelievable figment of my inflamed imagination, here are excerpts from what Larry Stein, who considers himself to be a stutterer, said: "The only rational thing I can come up with is that I want to keep that problem, [stuttering], in my back pocket and

*The dominance hierarchy in which we all live and interact is expressed in the old saw, "all men are created equal, but some are more equal than others."*

*I have searched in vain for a human interaction in which dominance is not a fundamental issue in how one speaks.*

just pull it out whenever I need to . . . . I had trouble dealing with . . . reality . . . , so I would shrink into this poor speech and succumb to what I began to call a stuttering fantasy . . . . I am struggling on the outside, but inside it is not so bad. It is kind of a relief. I'm kind of in my own time warp. While I'm having trouble no one can touch me. They can't, say, speak up; they wouldn't do that . . . . I've manipulated my life so that stuttering can relieve normal life-style tensions . . . . I don't have any other problems. If I happen to do well, they say isn't that great, the guy stutters and he can still tie his shoes . . . . I get out of these feelings of helplessness . . . . I've a rational excuse for not achieving. And I still get sympathy. Try and top that."

## Explaining the Unexplained

Seen this way, the "strangenesses" of stuttering don't seem so strange. They aren't necessary when one feels secure and able to cope in the real world, as when talking alone, or to animals, or to anyone who doesn't feel threatening.

And they aren't necessary when feeling totally defeated, or totally assertive. Here is what Larry Stein said when he gave up. By "giving up, I had also given up the need for excuses, the need to stutter." The assertive one said, "When I'm in a state dominated by approach drives, *or a state dominated by avoidance drives* [fear of assertiveness], my stuttering virtually disappears. When . . . the drives are roughly equal . . . , stuttering becomes part of my behavior." What these men said, in effect, is that stuttering vanishes at either extreme of submissiveness or assertiveness. It is when both occur together that stuttering results, which defines a dominance conflict. So fantasies and stuttering only emerge when a speaker feels intimidated and resentful. It could be having to speak to an audience, or use the phone, or talk to a parent—which is where it probably starts in the first place.

Viewed in this light, a strangeness reported by Dr. Charles Van Riper, the dean of clinicians, makes sense. A fearful nine-year-old boy prone to nightmares, bed wetting, and tics had begun to stutter. A few months after it began, the father, a butcher, brought home a basket of spoiled fish to fertilize his garden. As he came in, his son

*In nature, peace is generally preserved by each animal accepting its position in a dominance hierarchy. They do this with signals, including vocal signals. It is this vocal signal system which is a foundation of our spoken language.*

*"I caught him passing notes."*

By permission of Sandy Dean. Cartoon from *Science*.

*A dominance conflict depends on expectations of assertiveness, of the ability to control a speaking situation, whether our status be dominant or subordinate.*

ran to him while stuttering severely. The father, tired and irritated, couldn't stand it. He dumped the whole basket of rotten fish over the boy's head, and yelled at him, "Don't you never do no stuttering like that to me again," as if he had seen through why his son stuttered. The boy was never heard to stutter again; his protective shield was apparently stripped from him. A warning. This father's treatment may have worked in this case, but it is, nonetheless, to be deplored. Stripping anyone's protection from him is a dangerous business.

How can the feelings of guilt, shame, and failure, which plague people who stutter, make sense? Viewed rationally, as seen from the standpoint of the people who speak, why should they feel failure when they stutter? They have no responsibility for it. They don't want to do it. They simply can't prevent it, no matter how much willpower they have. But viewed in our light, the reason they feel failure is because, in some unknown way, they know deep down that they felt too intimidated to be openly assertive. Their guilt and shame is for giving in to their fears by letting stuttering be assertive for them, while at the same time letting it hide and protect them from standing out in the open.

Viewed this way, another puzzling aspect of stuttering makes sense. It tends to develop in children who are having trouble learning to meet society's standards for talking. Sometimes, it first appears after therapy for a speech problem. For children struggling against fear of being assertive in the first place, being corrected by parents as well as clinicians fuels their dominance conflict.

Being corrected adds speech to the activities they do not feel privileged to be assertive about, regardless of how resentful they may be.

Then there is the matter of why they try so hard to speak when hopelessly stuck. Since they hate to stutter so much, why don't they just stop until they can speak easily again? The answer we're looking at is that if they didn't need to control the conversation, they probably would stop and wait. But if they did, they would be failing to use their method of assertion—stuttering. The more assertive they feel, the harder they push when blocked.

Another thing that makes sense is why stutterers know by the tightening of their throats, mouths, or chests that they are about to stutter. One can lose control and stutter without throat, mouth, or chest tightening, so the reason for tightening cannot be a requirement of stuttering. That reason has to be something else which can result in stuttering. What makes sense is for that something else to be the dominance conflict. On one side is the need to be assertive, but pitted against it is the intimidating consequence of doing it openly. The tightening before stuttering, then, is akin to the tightening of speaking out in anger while holding back on it lest it be excessive.

Which leads to why stutterers who don't stutter seem to feel more disturbed than those who do. By hiding their stuttering when they tighten, they deprive themselves of the hidden assertiveness which is a powerful pay-off for those who stutter openly. Those who hide their stuttering have to swallow their resentment, or whatever feeling lies behind their assertiveness, without giving vent to it.

*When we feel that our listener accords us less respect than we feel we deserve, yet do not feel free to protest, then a dominance conflict sets in which can contribute mightily to stuttering.*

*The effect of conflict is a triple whammy—it retards how fast we can integrate syllables and sounds, while at the same time speeding up how fast we actually must integrate them, and then tightens throat, mouth, or chest. Severe stuttering is made from this combination.*

Finally, we're back to John. How does his transformation make sense? Apparently, through some deep manifestation of strength of which he knew nothing, and had no control over, he awoke to discover that, like a butterfly he had emerged from his cocoon of stuttering able to cope openly and assertively. It was when he realized that he was soaring without his protective shield of stuttering that he began to panic. He had no experience with being openly assertive. His safety net was gone. He gradually discovered during a month of acute anxiety that he could handle being aggressive in every dimension of his life. That was when he emerged as radically different from the quiet reticent person he had been. The panic he endured during his month's metamorphosis bespeaks the risk, and price, to be paid when one is stripped of protection, even when it's self induced. Had he not had some extraordinary well of courage, John undoubtedly could not have managed his rebirth.

Carl Dell tells a story he remembered from *Letting Go*:

> One day a naturalist who was passing by a barnyard inquired of the owner why it was that an eagle, the monarch of birds, was confined in the barnyard with the chickens.
>
> "Since I have given it chicken feed and trained it to be a chicken it has never learned to be anything else," said the farmer. "It behaves as a chicken behaves so it is no longer an eagle."
>
> "Still," insisted the naturalist, "it has the heart of an eagle, and it can surely be taught to fly." After talking it over, the two men agreed to find out whether this was possible.

Gently the naturalist took the eagle in his arms and said, "You belong to the sky and not the earth. Stretch forth your wings and fly." The eagle, however, was confused; she did not know who she was. Seeing the chickens eating their food, she jumped down to be with the chickens.

On the third day, the naturalist rose and took the eagle out of the barnyard and up to a high mountain. There he held the monarch of birds high above and encouraged her again saying, "You are an eagle, you belong to the sky and not to the earth, stretch forth your wings and fly." And the eagle began to tremble. Slowly she stretched forth her wings. At last with a triumphant cry, she soared to the heavens.

It may be that the eagle remembers the chickens with nostalgia, it may be that she occasionally visits the barnyard, but she has never returned to live the life of a chicken.

*Without a dominance conflict, there would be no need for the pay-offs of stuttering.*

Dell challenges stutterers to be like eagles, "to fly, to do great things, all because we have been given this disorder of stuttering. We have great decisions to make: Do I say the word or not? Do I talk to her or not? If it was easy, then we wouldn't be like eagles when we decide to stutter and not avoid." To Dell's statement I would add that the step John took, when overnight he gave up stuttering, was an act of some hidden reservoir of bravery, which made him the biggest eagle of them all.

I have told you all of this so that you can know what life can contain for probably most children who go on to become stutterers. If anything, stuttering becomes a barometer of their entire lives. The roots for such lives take hold in early childhood. As you can see, they contain far

*Sadly, reprimands are better than no attention. Because stuttering is required to get a response, stuttering is what receives the pay-off.*

more than just the mechanics of stuttering. They begin to grow before a child can even talk, let alone stutter.

So the prevention of stuttering before it starts comes down to how to encourage development of open assertiveness, beginning in the cradle. Children don't have to talk to be assertive. But they *do* have to feel secure. Before turning to the particulars of stuttering and how to stop it once it starts, let's begin by considering security and how it can be fostered. Stuttering *can* be prevented before it starts.

**GARFIELD** by Jim Davis

Reprinted by permission of UFS, Inc.

# Section II:
# Stuttering Prevented

*Once children think of themselves as stutterers, this handicapping image then protects any fantasies of being powerful.*

# Preventing Stuttering

Prevention of stuttering, truly being worth a pound—nay, a ton—of cure, demands that we begin with what parents can do to ensure that stuttering of the kind that can become permanent won't start in the first place, let alone turn your child into a stutterer. Later, we will talk about transient stuttering, which will be outgrown during childhood, usually within a year. For now, our concern is the young child, especially the very young child who hasn't even started to talk yet, who is at greatest risk of beginning to stutter without much chance of recovery. This is the insecure child who is also a shy child, with a history of stuttering in the family.

*When one can be easily assertive, can easily control a conversation, the attention stuttering provides is not needed. Similarly, power fantasies are not needed.*

None of this is to say that most children who are timid, or who come from families with a history of stuttering, will probably stutter. Most will not. But the risk for these children is greater.

From all that has been said so far, it should be apparent that the roots of lifelong conflict-driven stuttering invade virtually every aspect of life. It is vastly more than just the irritation of involuntary disruptions of attempts to express ideas, it involves one's whole identity. More

**53**

*To cope, insecure children are likely to develop protective fantasies, which stuttering can help preserve.*

specifically, it involves the right to talk firmly, with the conviction that one is as free to be in control as anyone else. When that conviction is in jeopardy, then the soil has been fertilized for the roots of the stutterer to grow. Fed by a dominance conflict, they will spread.

Remember, too, that not much about such stuttering is, in fact, what it appears to be. It does not lend itself to rational understanding, nor to rational solutions. To wit: I have yet to meet adults who stutter who do not wish they didn't. And yet they do. And they can't *not* stutter, given the right circumstance. And that's a puzzle. Most of the time they speak normally, but given a certain situation, a certain listener, their tongues are suddenly stuck to the roofs of their mouths. And when they do recover, it is as much a mystery as why they stuttered in the first place. Even their good days and bad days are a mystery. As witness to the futility of rationality, no one to my knowledge, despite numberless rational attempts, has ever claimed a credible cure for chronic stuttering. Everything important about it

# Calvin and Hobbes                                    by Bill Watterson

Calvin & Hobbes copyright 1990 Universal Press Syndicate. Reprinted with permission. All rights reserved.

seems to go on so far under the surface that even the person who stutters can't see it. What they think they feel doesn't seem to match up with how their bodies react.

All of this suggests that the seeds of stuttering are planted so early that children at risk are not yet able to recognize, let alone think clearly, about what is happening to them. They experience, they respond, but there is little they can do to prevent the planting of seeds that will make them vulnerable to stuttering. Those seeds are insecurity and its twin, shyness.

*Without pay-offs, the addictiveness of stuttering dwindles to insignificance.*

## Insecurity and Shyness

### Infancy

One of the temperament characteristics children are born with is a tendency toward assertiveness or timidity. If the tendency is toward shyness, the need for careful nurturance from birth is of special importance if he is to feel secure as he develops. A child who grows up feeling secure and important is a child who will not be vulnerable to stuttering, regardless of how timid he may be inherently.

Any child can be insecure. Children can be born with temperaments from timid to aggressive, but they are not predestined to be insecure. That is a product of how they were parented. Some of the best parents I have known have raised insecure children through no fault of their own. In each case, the problem was that they were unable to respond to their infants when they were needed. In

*The self-concept of being a stutterer emerges when one becomes addicted to using stuttering to gain the rewards of assertiveness without the risk of doing it openly.*

one case, the mother was hospitalized with tuberculosis after her son was born. In another, the mother was struggling to make ends meet, manage a newborn baby, and follow her husband from training camp to training camp during World War II. Both of these families had more children later who grew up as secure as one could wish.

But infants know nothing about why a parent is not available when needed. The effect on a child will be the same when a parent is needed but is unavailable, whether because of circumstances, because of family strife, because the child is not wanted, because the parents want the baby to meet their needs rather than the other way around. To cope, insecure children are likely to develop protective fantasies, which stuttering can help preserve. But protection of these fantasies with stuttering does not begin until children begin to think of themselves as stutterers. It is when they have the self-image of handicapped stutterer that the actual stuttering becomes protective of that image. Until then, stuttering is not particularly troublesome.

Research has shown that the key to giving children security is being responsive to their needs from birth.* The foundation of security is the child's knowledge that he can control his world. During infancy, you *are* his world. You

---

*Dr. Mary Ainsworth, who pioneered this landmark research, has published it mainly in the professional literature. If you want to read about it you could start with a popular article about her work which appeared in *The Atlantic*, February, 1990. If you want to read Dr. Ainsworth's own writing you could start with an article of hers in the 1989 *American Psychologist*, pages 709–716.

only have to respond when your baby wants you to respond. If you respond most of the time when you feel like it, but not when your child needs it, then you are being intrusive. Even if parents did all the right things—picking up their infants, kissing, cuddling, cooing and all the rest—but often ignored their children's requests for such attention, then unlimited love under that condition would not teach them that they can obtain affection when they need it. They will learn that lesson, which is the foundation of security, as they learn that they can incite anger as well as evoke love—when they need it. With security comes reduced risk of stuttering.

*Once established, stuttering becomes a protective pay-off for the fantasy images associated with being a stutterer.*

Of course, such a prescription for shyness and insecurity is simplistic. Successful parenthood is no more straightforward than a successful ball game. There is no such thing as perfect parenthood anymore than there is a perfect ball game. Mistakes are inevitable. But the thrust of successful parenthood, as measured at least by freedom from stuttering, follows the gist of the foregoing prescription, especially in the earliest years.

## Older Childhood

Stuttering, however, can also begin in later childhood. How can it be prevented in those ages? The same principles we just discussed apply. But they are considerably more elaborate. Deal with shyness and you deal with insecurity, so we'll concentrate on shyness as it contributes to stuttering in older children. Shyness is a broad subject

*"My thoughts . . . change color . . . It's like I'm constantly painting masterpieces, and the only way I can protect them is to spoil them with stuttering so that people won't know for sure that they weren't masterpieces."*
*(a stutterer)*

in itself. Fortunately, it has been dealt with in depth in *A Parent's Guide to the Shy Child*, which is based on Dr. Philip Zimbardo's experience and research at the Stanford Shyness Clinic.

Let's begin by agreeing on characteristics in older children by which shyness can be recognized. It is a natural reticence, a "people phobia," which feeds on fear: fear of evaluation, fear of social failure, fear of rejection, fear of intimacy. Shy people are likely to feel more sensitive, introspective, guilty, inadequate, moody. They are less likely to feel likable, expressive, interesting, attractive, charming, satisfied.

Having said all of this about how shy people feel, many do not wear their shyness for all the world to see. They can hide it and play the role of extrovert—in adult years as actors, teachers, lecturers. This includes such celebrities as Jimmy Carter, John Travolta, Carol Burnett, and Johnny Carson. But when the spotlight on their public self goes off, they revert to their shy private world. All of this subterfuge to hide shyness, like stuttering, begins in early childhood.

Shyness does not necessarily run in families any more than stuttering does. Another strong parallel to stuttering is the type of condition which triggers it: strangers, authorities, parents, large groups, giving a speech, low status, being evaluated, new situations, needing help.

But one thing is reasonably certain. How much success or how many failures children have growing up will play a big role in how shyness affects their lives. Infants who had to cry long and loud for affection and attention were learning failure. So, too, with older children. John, whose story you may recall (p. 31), remembers aching for his mother to hold him and speak lovingly, but all he got were her matter-of-fact protestations that "of course" she loved him.

Even as adults, who does not crave being held, cuddled, touched lovingly? Who does not crave being encouraged to talk—about themselves, about anything and everything? Who does not crave being cared for just because you are you, not for what you've done or the affection you've earned for being "good." Filling these needs is vital for all of us. For children, their lives are shaped by their success or failure with such cravings.

## How Parents Can Help

To determine how you are contributing to your child's ability to outgrow or to reinforce tendencies to shyness—and in all probability to stuttering—ask yourself such questions as these:

- Do I respond to needs for affection and attention only when I feel like it, or when my child wants it?
- Am I too permissive or too authoritarian?
- How often do I really talk with my child with undivided attention?
- How often do I really listen? (One little shy boy who was starting to stutter could not get his father's attention when he was reading, so the boy finally, in desperation, hit him on the foot with a hammer. He

*"While I'm having trouble no one can touch me. They can't, say, speak up; they wouldn't do that  .... I've manipulated my life so that stuttering can relieve normal lifestyle tensions .... I don't have any other problems. If I happen to do well, they say isn't that great, the guy stutters and he can still tie his shoes .... I get out of these feelings of helplessness. I've got a rational excuse for not achieving. And I still get sympathy. Try and top that."*
*(a stutterer)*

*Not much about stuttering is what it appears to be. It does not lend itself to rational understanding, nor to rational solutions.*

got his attention, all right—more, in fact, than he bargained for.)

- Can my child talk to me about anything, or are there taboo subjects?
- How often do I make my child feel special?
- How often do I give others more affection or attention than I give my shy child?
- How often do I show my child that I can be trusted?
- Do I teach my child tolerance by example?
- Do I preserve my child's dignity when I discipline?
- Do the limits I set send a message of caring and understanding?
- Do I set an example of fairness and honesty?
- Do I refrain from labeling behavior that bothers me, such as shyness and stuttering?

Granting that timid children will remain inherently timid, our underlying assumption is that by reducing shyness, conditions contributing to stuttering will also be reduced. So what else can you do to help? For starters, set realistic expectations. If they are too low, there is no challenge. If too high, the risk of failure is too great. When the challenge is just right, accomplishing it is exhilarating. Such a challenge has to have some risk of failure if meeting it is to be exhilarating. The probability of success, however, must outweigh the risk. This means, of course, that only when a child is ready for a new challenge should you expect it to be undertaken.

The price of pushing for performance is high. For one thing, it says that affection depends on achievement. That's a heavy burden for anyone, and especially for a child. And yet, who doesn't want one's child to excel? There is a vast difference, however, between encouraging and pushing. Parents who encourage find satisfaction in whatever achievements their child manages. A grade of "C" in school may be a bigger challenge for one child than an "A" would be for another. The joy is in seeing the child's performance at whatever level can be achieved. I remember watching two fathers at a Little League game. One beamed when his son got in the game in its closing minutes, even though he struck out. The other was hoarse from shouting directions at his son who played the entire game. His team won, but the father was not satisfied with the boy's performance. The boy was still being lectured as they drove away.

When parents push, they are living out their own desires and frustrations through their children. It is not by accident that when you find a child prodigy, you often find a parent pushing for achievement. Predictably, early burnout is common. In one case, an extraordinarily talented quarterback whose father had groomed him from infancy, who was the hero of his college, turned his back on a football career and became an artist.

Tailoring expectations to levels at which the child is challenged, but yet can succeed, is the essence of prevention of stuttering for the same reason it is the essence of recovery. Even significant improvement in people who

*"Ironically, the best period of speech in my entire life was when I was terribly depressed. I had given up on life and I felt pain, I felt anguish, I felt helplessness . . . . I was no longer competing with anyone, including the older members of my family. I had just totally given up."*
*(a stutterer)*

*Hardly a description, this statement, of how one would expect a person who stutters to feel when freed of stuttering.*

*Stutterers can't **not** stutter, given the right circumstances. And that's a puzzle. Most of the time they speak normally, but given a certain situation, a certain listener, their tongues are suddenly stuck to the roofs of their mouths.*

have stuttered for years lies in finding courage to meet challenges they long ago learned to fear and avoid. When shy children discover the exhilaration of facing a challenge and succeeding, they have taken a giant step away from shyness—and away from the probability of stuttering. When coping with the real world straight out and openly becomes a source of satisfaction rather than fear, that is when the need for stuttering to protect fantasies of power dwindles into insignificance.

The basis of security changes as children grow. As babies, it depends on their success in getting their parents to respond promptly to their needs when they announce them. If they are cuddled mainly when the parents feel like it instead of when the infants want it, then they learn that they are unsuccessful in controlling parental responses. Later, after they can talk, the ability of children to command parental attention with elementary speech will become their measure of success. Then, after they are capable of entering into conversations, during the latter preschool years, their ability to control family conversations will be the measure. Finally, with entry into school, ability to enter and control conversations among peers will become the ongoing determinant of how privileged they feel to speak out.

Prevention of failed efforts to communicate successfully is difficult at best. Remember that communication begins at birth. Until speech develops, babies only have a signal system, but it is an ancient one, tested in the crucible of evolution. If they cannot succeed with it, then the foundation on which speech will be built will be shaky.

From then on, as growing children, they will carry the burden of trying to disprove that their earliest conviction is false: that they are not worthy enough to command attention. Their life, then, will begin on a premise of insecurity. Obviously, the best chance for prevention is in infancy. If parents could act on this recommendation before speech appears, let alone stuttering, then inherently dangerous conflict-driven stuttering would not begin in the first place.

*When they do recover, it is as much a mystery as why they stuttered in the first place.*

# Section III: Stuttering Stopped

*"Once I start talking I just can't stop. I love words. They're the most powerful, beautiful things I know."* This was spoken by a person who stuttered severely.

# What Should Be Stopped
# and What Shouldn't?

Before considering how stuttering can be stopped once started, we need to clarify speech disruptions that feel natural from those that feel like stuttering. This distinction is important because everyone has speech disruptions, and some of them sound like stuttering. When we talk about preventing stuttering from becoming permanent, we will not be trying to prevent natural speech disruptions. That would be impossible to begin with, and the result would be unnatural if we succeeded. Being fluent without exception may be desirable for TV announcers who are reading teleprompters, but in normal conversation, perfect fluency is almost freakish.

We won't even be concerned with severity of speech disruptions, because natural disruptions can be severe and still not be experienced as stuttered. Even when they qualify as stuttering, one may not be aware of them, so they, too, are not a problem. What we will consider in this section is what can be done to minimize, if not stop, stuttering that is relatively harmless. This is

*Stuttering was apparently stronger than inflicting severe electrical shock as a method of assertion and retaliation.*

**67**

*The strangest part of all was John's overnight transformation. Before, he was one whose stuttering was terribly severe and who personally was the gentlest of men. After, he was completely fluent and uninhibitedly aggressive. Why did such a wildly improbable change occur? What could have happened? No one knew, least of all John.*

the stuttering that may be of more concern to you than to your child. Section IV will be devoted to the stuttering that can become a severe problem.

Stated briefly, the children most likely to outgrow stuttering with which you may be concerned are disrupted for reasons they can be aware of, in particular, linguistic stuttering. Although they can readily recognize why their speech is halted when they have not yet figured out phrasing, word selection, or pronunciation, this all happens automatically most of the time. When children are under time pressure (pressure to rush), however, they can be oblivious of obvious causes of disruption. Under such circumstances they can exhibit what we could logically call linguistic stuttering. It is probably this type of stuttering, for the most part, which is outgrown, usually within a year. The reason for this probability is that language maturation is almost complete by puberty, and that is also the stage of development at which stuttering will be mainly outgrown if it is going to be outgrown.

Another major feature of children who will outgrow stuttering is that they tend to be secure. Those who enjoy talking want to speak out when they have something to say. Like most of us who have automatic conversation starters, such as "uhhh," or "you know," or "like," or "wellll," which have nothing to do with what we're going to say, children, too, use similar devices to alert people to their announcements. These can be any kind of vocal starter, including ones which can sound like stuttering. As you may recall, this is what Alex did.

Along the same line, children have a good chance of outgrowing stuttering if it occurs mainly when they are excited, angry, are trying to make a point, or are talking fast in heated conversations. These are natural states for even the calmest and happiest of children. Yet, they can just as effectively turn disruptions for any cause into stuttering. With puberty, however, the need for sophistication begins. One has to turn away from childhood abandon, from letting it all hang out; one has to become cool. (Undoubtedly it is no longer hip to be "cool," so I probably am neither cool nor hip to talk of "hip" or "cool.") Be that as it may, the effect of puberty is the same. With it is likely to come a less hectic talking rate, which would predictably reduce stuttering.

Summing up, children who are confident, secure, and assertive, who are *not* selective about where or with whom they stutter, who like to talk, speak out without hesitation, compete successfully, and pay little attention to whatever stuttering may occur, are the children most likely to outgrow it.

Stuttering by itself is not that much of a problem. Unless the speaker makes it a big deal, stuttering can occur frequently, and even severely, without being very bothersome. If only stuttering is involved, it will be no more than a nuisance to a child, or even later to an adult. Certainly, stuttering alone is not cause to build one's life around it.

But becoming a stutterer is something else entirely. The only thing it has in common with stuttering is that, superficially, it is what seems to be the problem. In reality, the stuttering is only the tip of the iceberg. It is the function stuttering serves, its addictive pay-offs, which make it so difficult to cure.

*All of these "strangenesses" seem to boil down to three things: fantasies of power, with speech as a tool for achieving that power; stuttering as the method of protecting a powerful self-image; and stuttering as an effective method of being in control without being openly assertive, aggressive, or angry.*

*Fantasies and stuttering only emerge when a speaker feels intimidated and resentful.*

In reality, then, we have two objectives. The obvious one is to minimize stuttering, and to stop it in so far as possible. By far and away the most important objective, though, is to prevent it, for whatever reasons, from acquiring pay-offs. When those pay-offs become an important tool for coping with assertiveness, then the person who had been stuttering has become a stutterer.

None of the strategies we will discuss are new. Although my colleagues and I have used all of them, they are not exclusively ours by any stretch of the imagination. There are many ingenious clinicians around the world who have devised effective techniques for preventing and treating stuttering. The strategies we will consider have all been successful when used appropriately. The puzzle has always been, why do they work sometimes, but not others? This book is intended to provide answers to that question.

What *is* new will be a guideline for using these strategies so that they can be expected to succeed. What will work with one set of causes cannot be expected to be effective with all others. To be successful, strategies must be tailored to the causes of stuttering in a particular child.

## Stopping Stuttering

We are now at the bottom line. What can parents do, and how can they do it?   Because I want to talk to you specifically about your child I will need to use either "he" or "she." I will assume that your child is a boy because so many more boys stutter than girls. If it is your daughter who stutters, please translate my "he" into "she."

Interestingly, the traditional lament about treatment is that there are as many therapies as there are therapists. This is not an idle lament. Thirty years ago in California alone, over 100 different therapies for stuttering were reported. Although the techniques for stopping it can be numerous, the purposes to be accomplished are limited. To stop stuttering requires a tight focus.

*If stutterers didn't need to control the conversation, they probably would stop and wait. But if they did, they would be failing to use their method of assertion—stuttering.*

## Guide to Strategies

The following guide is provided for you to make a preliminary selection of the Strategy most likely to help your child stop stuttering. Three strategies are included in Section III. To begin, see if any of these seem to apply and choose the one that probably fits your child best. When in doubt, start with the one with the lowest number which fits. It will be the easiest.

*Strategy 1* is for children who have a good chance of outgrowing their stuttering without much help. If they do *not* have all of the following characteristics, a different Strategy will probably be needed.

Children are more likely to outgrow stuttering if they:

- feel confident.
- feel secure.
- feel assertive.

*The more assertive stutterers feel, the harder they push when blocked.*

- feel privileged to speak out.
- are not much affected by where they stutter or with whom.
- successfully compete for attention.
- do not feel guilty or care if they stutter
- stutter mainly when excited, talk fast, or have something important they want to say.
- recover within a year.
- do not stutter more with some people than others.
- can speak fast without stuttering when talking to themselves alone.

*Strategy 2* is for children who have stuttered for more than a year and meet most of the qualifications for Strategy 1. To recover, they will probably need help. Strategy 2 will be appropriate if they:

- stutter only when excited.
- do not stutter more with some people than with others.

*Strategy 3* is the same as Strategy 2 except that in addition to excitement, it is designed to help children who stutter when outside pressure is applied such as when competing to enter a conversation.

None of these three strategies is intended to help a child cope with conflict. Stuttering more with some people than others is a key sign of conflict. The strategy for that problem will be presented in Section IV. You may notice that discussion of strategies increases as their numbers go up. This is because more is involved in coping with children in conflict (Strategies 4–6), who are at greatest risk, than with relatively secure children who are likely to recover from stuttering (Strategies 1–3).

## Who Will Recover Without Help?
## Strategy 1: Help Outgrow Stuttering

*One can lose control and stutter without throat, mouth, or chest tightening, so the reason for tightening cannot be a requirement of stuttering.*

### Example

Jason's stuttering was typical of children who will outgrow early stuttering. His mother said "he hit the ground running" when he was born. He wouldn't go to sleep at night unless he was rocked or taken for a drive. One night, his mother was so frustrated that the whole side of his crib collapsed as she rocked him furiously. He was always into everything. Which is to say that he was anything but a nice quiet little baby.

His development, however, was unique, and was probably revealing of his independence from birth. He didn't crawl when he was supposed to. Then, without preamble, he started walking. After he could do this, then he crawled—backwards. Of greater concern was the parent's fear that he was deaf. The father even resorted to banging pots and pans and slamming doors to see if Jason would react. He didn't. After more than six months of hardly a sound, he began long babbled "conversations" and singing while he splashed bath water over his mother. From then on he was hardly ever quiet, certainly not deaf.

*The tightening before stuttering is akin to the tightening of speaking out in anger while holding back on it lest it be excessive.*

By three years, he was talking incessantly. As his sentences got longer and the grammar more complex, his speech began to fill up with hesitations while he figured out how to say what he wanted to say. About six months after starting nursery school, the teacher reported he had begun to stutter. What happened was that Jason and another boy with whom he was vying for leadership had gotten into a big argument. In pushing to control the dispute, Jason's sentences were often disrupted by sound and word repetitions (w-w-w-well and but-but-but-but, for instance).

Once Jason's parents were alerted, they realized that he did have repetitions at home as well, especially when excited or angry. When he tried to get into a conversation, his repetitions sometimes turned into blocked words. He certainly sounded as if he were stuttering, as he probably was, but he didn't seem bothered. After leadership disputes were resolved, the stuttering waned, only to surface again briefly when he started kindergarten. Today, as an adult, Jason has no recollection of ever stuttering.

## Procedure

Step 1. Determine if your child shows any exceptions to the dozen conditions for spontaneous recovery. If he does, more help may be needed. Nonetheless, start with Strategy 1. If it is successful, it will save time and effort.

Step 2. If your child wonders why his speech is occasionally disrupted, tell him it is nothing to worry about, that everyone does it at least a little sometimes (which they do).

Step 3. Console yourself with the realization that this problem is not severe, that your child probably will not react to it as stuttering if you do not, and that it will likely be outgrown. Nothing is apt to be wrong with him, so do not treat him as if he has a problem. Chances are he does not. You can make it one, however, by telling him, for instance, to slow down, relax, take your time, or think before you talk. Your intentions would undoubtedly be good, but for reasons we will discuss later, these are among the worst things you can do.

*Prevention of stuttering before it starts comes down to how to encourage development of open assertiveness, beginning in the cradle.*

Other "don'ts" are recommended by the American Speech-Language-Hearing Association.

- Don't criticize or correct his speech.
- Don't call him a "stutterer".
- Don't complete his sentences.
- Don't interrupt him.
- Don't look distressed when you hear what sounds like stuttering (it may not be).
- Don't call attention to his speech.
- Don't put his speech on display.

Step 4. Determine if your child is slower than most other children in learning to talk. If his language development worries you, consult a speech-language clinician.

Step 5. Observe whether his speech models (you and your family) talk to him with big words or long complex

*Children don't have to talk to be assertive. But they do have to feel secure.*

sentences. If so, use shorter sentences and simpler words to see if it makes talking easier for him.

Most childhood stuttering, for which Strategy 1 is appropriate, will probably be outgrown. The only problem with exuberance, whether excitement, anger, or whatever, is that it gives urgency to a child's need to command a conversation. Moreover, when excited or angry, for instance, one is preoccupied with the message and not with the linguistic processes of assembling it. Linguistic disruptions occur when children try to talk when they do not yet know the word they are trying to say. Even though the cause is readily available to awareness, children are likely to be oblivious of that cause as they speak excitedly, especially preschool children. They may stumble in ways which can sound like stuttering as they plow ahead, and which may be experienced as loss of control, but they are not likely to lead to lasting difficulty.

## Who Will Need Help?
## Strategy 2: Reduce Excitement Effects

In addition to the vast majority of children who stutter for awhile and then outgrow it, a small group will continue who can be helped with Strategies 2 or 3. These are secure children who show none of the three essential signs of vulnerability to become stutterers: insecurity/ difficulty asserting self in conversation/stuttering gains attention. You need to be aware of two considerations when using either strategy. One is that a possible cause of continued speech disruptions is a limitation imposed by the brain on how fast your child can speak without triggering stuttering. That limitation could be caused by heredity or brain injury. No medical treatment for changing that limit is known, so it would have to be accepted as being relatively permanent.

The other consideration is that when excited, people automatically speak faster. You probably couldn't change this reaction in the first place, and wouldn't want to if you could. Couple these two conditions together and what would be bound to happen is stuttering occurring whenever your child exceeds this limit. The bad news is that this limit may be slower than he normally speaks. If it is, then you will need Strategy 2 or 3 to help him use a slower normal rate. If stuttering only happens when he's exuberant, then the good news is that he probably won't even notice that it has occurred, it will happen automatically in the midst of his excitement. Certainly you do not want to make a problem where there is not one. If your child shows signs of disturbance when disrupted, be calmly honest; openly acknowledge the difficulty he is having without making it a big thing. Do not try to protect him by pretending that he does not feel stuck when his frustration tells you he does. He will read silence as a sign that something is seriously wrong with him. On the other hand, if he is untroubled about his disruptions, then you should follow his lead and be equally untroubled. The day will come when he can find relief in understanding the cause of his stuttering.

*Stuttering can be prevented before it starts.*

*None of this is to say that most children who are timid, or who come from families with a history of stuttering, will probably stutter. Most will not. But the risk for these children is greater.*

## Example

Diane began stuttering when she began to express herself in words a few months after her second birthday. Not only did Diane's mother stutter, but so does her father, older brother and younger sister. Although heredity undoubtedly plays a major role in the stuttering of this family, Diane is the only member who fits Strategy 2. She only stutters when exuberant.

Unlike her mother, who talks a blue streak, Diane is more like her father, who tends to be calm and deliberate. Fortunately for her, both her father and brother provide her with good models for speaking slowly and easily— both have to watch how fast they talk if they are to keep their stuttering from spiraling out of control. Diane, now in 5th grade, knows what happens to her speech when she gets excited. Although stuttering is irritating when it does occur, she uses it as a signal that she's talking too fast. Knowing that it will stop when she slows down keeps it from being much of a problem for her.

## Procedure

Step 1. Determine if a constitutional limitation exists on how fast your child can talk before he stutters. Make this determination by observing whether he ever stutters when talking aloud when alone. If he does, then observe how fast he talks when stuttering occurs. When he talks faster than this in conversation is when he is most likely to stutter. Step 1 is for *your* information. Please, *do not use it as license to tell your child to slow down.* You can turn normal speech disruptions into a major problem if you do.

If no limit exists on how fast your child can talk alone without stuttering, then a higher-number strategy may be needed. Before proceeding to it, though, use Strategy 2. It can only help, and may be successful. If it isn't, you'll know soon enough, and then you can move ahead.

*Freedom from stuttering involves the right to talk firmly, with the conviction that one is as free to be in control as anyone else.*

## Preschool Children

A mother of a four-year-old boy told me that she had her best success modeling unhurried speech by creating a story together. I commend her strategy to you. They did this every day at nap time or bedtime. She said he was most cooperative when he knew it delayed the inevitable nap. They would begin with "Once upon a time . . . ." Some days they would create very low-key stories (which made slow speeds easy). Other days they would test their ability to keep speeds slow by creating high-energy stories with his super heroes fighting. He remained attentive during these stories for 5 to 10 minutes. If she forgot the story, he would ask for one, so he did enjoy them.

## School Children

Older children can learn to recognize that when they speed up their speech, stuttering will occur. Once they can

*The reason they feel failure is because, in some unknown way, they know deep down that they felt too intimidated to be openly assertive.*

see clearly that something they do and can control causes stuttering, then the scariest part of the problem has been prevented, even if they continue to stutter. If stuttering persists, then move on to Strategy 3.

### Strategy 3: Reduce Family Pressure Effects

Although designed primarily for constitutionally imposed speed limits on speech, Strategy 3 is equally applicable when linguistic uncertainty is the cause of speech disruptions. If your child fits the following two conditions, in addition to those for Strategy 2, then use Strategy 3:

- Stutters during normal conversation as well as when excited.

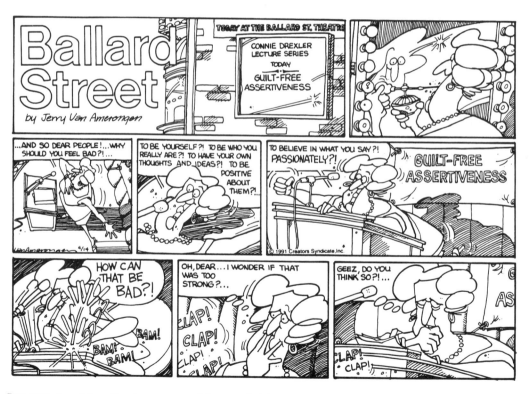

By permission of Jerry Van Amerongen and Creators Syndicate.

- Severity of stuttering depends on fast speech rate, not on to whom he is talking.

## *Example*

Diane has an older brother, Ted, who also stutters for genetic reasons, just as Diane does. The difference is that Ted not only stutters when excited or arguing, he also stutters when he tries to get into a conversation, or a talk with his mother. The common thread running through all of these situations is that his speech speeds up in all of them. With his mother, he has a difficult time talking slowly enough not to be disrupted by his genetic limitations when she is zipping along a mile a minute. With family conversations, he has to rush to get into them. This is especially annoying because, he complains, whenever Diane starts to talk, everybody stops to listen. When he tries to talk, nobody listens, at least as he sees it.

Ted is entering puberty, a critical age at which peer pressures and opinions are magnified. Whereas earlier, his stuttering was only an annoyance which didn't seem to trouble him much, now it is becoming a problem he tries to hide. This is the danger. The more he tries to avoid it, the more he will fear it. Although he had therapy, he is only now starting to take it seriously. If he becomes sufficiently convinced that his stuttering is triggered by speeding up, then he has a chance of containing it at the annoyance level.

This will be difficult, of course, particularly during his teens, if he is to participate in all of the excited and

*When the conviction of the right to be assertive is in jeopardy, then the soil has been fertilized for the roots of the stutterer to grow. Fed by a dominance conflict, they will spread.*

*If my ideas are right, addictiveness is at the root of becoming a stutterer. To prevent this identity would require nipping the bud of this addictiveness in childhood before it takes root.*

emotional chatter of those years. His best chance of coming through with the fewest scars will be to demonstrate to himself that by keeping speed down, he can talk without disruption. Knowing this, he can speed up and stutter without feeling helpless—he will know that if he chooses to speak slowly the stuttering will vanish.

## Procedure

### Preschool Children

Step 1. Read the following strategy carefully and, together as parents, decide whether changing the lifestyle of your family will be something you can actually do. By virtue of reading this book, I assume that you are eager to prevent your child's stuttering from becoming a life-long problem. For you, it is not a question of wanting to help, it will be a matter of will. Make no mistake, to implement this strategy well enough for it to succeed will require great determination. Not that any given step requires doing anything you cannot do. It is the necessity of changing so many small things you do which will be difficult. The benefit can be equally as great as the challenge. Without intervention the stuttering for which Strategy 3 is designed is likely to continue. This is because the constitutional cause of disruptions will probably exist for life with no known way of changing it. The reward is that if you can achieve the changes for which the following steps are designed, the probability of stuttering can be reduced to manageable size, if not stopped entirely.

Step 2. Call a family meeting to obtain agreement that everyone needs to lead a less hectic, more relaxed life. Do not present this as a meeting to help your child who stutters. It is vitally important that he feel that he is just one member of the family, no more privileged than anyone else, who is joining with everyone to make a family decision. The potential arguments you can present for a relaxed life style are numerous. Here are a few suggestions:

- Reduced stress for improved health
- Improved relationships within the family
- Improved digestion
- Improved enjoyment of life.

Assuming that as parents, you agree on the importance of this prevention strategy, then the purpose of the family meeting is to enlist participation of other family members, even if they are reluctant. If anyone asks if this is being done to help your child who stutters, you can reply honestly, "It will be as good for him as it will be for the rest of us."

Step 3. Describe how you will accomplish this easier life style as a Relaxation Game. As a family, select for

*Seeds of stuttering are planted so early that children at risk are not yet able to recognize, let alone think clearly, about what is happening to them.*

*Children experience, they respond, but there is little they can do to prevent what will make them vulnerable to stuttering.*

a starter a 15- to 30-minute period in which most of you are together, and are relatively relaxed, possibly during or after dinner. Then explain the rules of the game you will use to learn to go easy:

- Everyone has to do everything in slow motion during the relaxation period. In addition to talking slow and easy, walk, gesture, chew, swallow and do everything else slow and easy.

- Choose a "hot" family topic to get everyone talking as heatedly as possible during each period. The challenge is to talk heatedly in slow motion.

- Anyone who breaks the slow-motion rule doing anything pays a penalty of, say, a poker chip. If everyone starts with the same number of chips, the game can be carried over from period to period until someone runs out of chips. At that point, the winner is whoever has the most. Then start a new game.

- A chip is earned each time anyone enters the conversation.

- A penalty of two chips is assessed for anyone who butts into anyone else's conversation.

- Everyone is equally privileged to call a penalty, but if called too fast, it, too, can draw a penalty. Disputed decisions are adjudicated by the other members.

- Anyone who tells anyone else to slow down outside the relaxation period is penalized two chips. The purpose of this rule is to discourage everyone from telling your child who stutters to slow down. The cardinal rule, for you as a parent especially, is to NEVER TELL A CHILD WHO STUTTERS TO SLOW DOWN. The entire purpose of this game is to provide a condition for unrushed speech in which your child is on equal footing with everyone else. Within the context of the game he could be penalized for speeding up, just as everyone else could be. But he is as privileged to penalize others as they are to penalize him, so he is not singled out. Everyone is in the same slow boat pulling on the same oars together— slowly. The object is to set up conditions in which he will automatically slow down without thinking about it. UNDER NO CIRCUM- STANCE SHOULD HE EVER BE SINGLED OUT TO SLOW DOWN.

*The seeds of stuttering are insecurity and its twin, shyness.*

Step 4. Try to make the game enjoyable enough that your child who stutters, as well as the rest of your family, looks forward to it. If you can achieve that level of interest, then you can move ahead at whatever pace enjoyment can be maintained. If interest lags, then a criterion for the next step is that your child keep an unrushed enough pace during the relaxation period to have few penalties and little stuttering.

Step 5. Once your family has mastered a relaxed supper (or whenever) you can add another occasion. Before adding occasions, stay with the one you are

*Children can be born with temperaments from timid to aggressive, but they are not predestined to be insecure. That is a product of how they were parented.*

mastering until you find yourselves automatically slowing down. If you move ahead before an occasion has become automatic, you will have to think about going slowly during two or three occasions. This can become so burdensome that your family could start tightening instead of relaxing. So before proceeding to any other occasion, be sure that you and your family are succeeding effortlessly at what you have attempted. When ready, select another occasion of about 30 minutes and extend the game to it, so that you now have two periods daily.

Step 6. You may need to add another occasion or two to your daily schedule before taking the next step. This would be to extend the game to an entire day, probably on the weekend. When that is successful, add another day. Keep adding days until you can go for an entire week. Then take a week's vacation from the game. Stay with this schedule, one week on, one week off, until the slow pace of the week on carries over to the week off.

Step 7. Use the additional suggestions of the American Speech-Language-Hearing Association:

- In addition to speaking slow and easy, pause frequently.
- Talk to him alone without distractions or competition.
- Give him time to answer a question before asking another.

Step 8. If you find after a month that your best efforts are not successful in extending a slow enough pace throughout the day to reduce your child's stuttering, then you may want to consult a speech clinician for help in easing the family pace. With young children, direct therapy is not as effective as the example parents set at home. So if you do seek help for a young child, it should be to help you to become effective models.

*He tried to tell his mother how hurt and angry he was. He resented her for undercutting his attempts to tell her that all she gave him were words he couldn't believe.*

We must assume that children who fit Strategy 3 are secure within themselves. Given that assumption, the major problem which can arise, and be altered, is within the family. It is the problem of the family's effect on a child's habitual speaking rate.

## CATHY by Cathy Guisewite

Cathy copyright 1990 Cathy Guisewite. Reprinted with permission of Universal Press Syndicate.

*Research has shown that the key to giving children security is being responsive to their needs from birth.*

To my knowledge, no one knows what controls habitual speech rate. Certain brain disorders can speed it up or slow it down, but whether it is affected by heredity or not is an open question. From what I have observed, my strong suspicion is that it reflects the speaking rate which prevails in the family, for whatever reasons. Because rate fluctuates to fit the situation, it can be altered. It is not set in concrete. The probability is that if parents slow down, children will follow their model. Because much is to be gained if this is true, we will make that assumption for this prevention strategy.

The effect of a genetic or brain injury predisposition to stutter is to retard the rate at which syllables can be generated. When the speaking rate exceeds the syllable rate, involuntary disruption occurs. As we have just seen, when time pressure is driven by excitement, the consequent stuttering lasts only as long as exuberance drives up the speaking rate. A child can learn to live with that.

Habitual speaking rates that exceed syllable rates, however, are infinitely more difficult to live with. Under this condition there is no relief from disruption when speaking automatically. Even the healthiest, most secure children will react badly to this circumstance. They are at high risk of having stuttering as a life-long problem. Their only salvation is to develop a slow enough automatic speaking rate that stuttering is not often triggered, except, perhaps, during exuberance.

Prevention would be difficult enough if the child, alone, could accomplish it. But that is virtually impossible. For starters, the temptation for the family to admonish the child to "slow down" will be received as a power play of the worst order. Even when it is honestly done "for the child's own good," it will generate resentment, not slower speech. It is a "do as I say, not as I do" admonition *to be avoided at all times.*

The most important reason children cannot slow down alone is because they will reflect the family's speaking rate. When children with a genetic predisposition to stutter are disrupted most of the time with any member of their family, the stuttering speaks loudly of the family's speaking rate being too fast. Of course, being too fast for one child who stutters is not necessarily too fast for another. The "too-fast" rule is not fixed, it is determined by the rate at which stuttering occurs in *your* child.

Preventing development of stuttering requires establishing a stutter-free speaking rate that is automatic. If children have to think about speaking slowly, rather than about what they are saying, sooner or later they will conclude that they would rather stutter. Consider for yourself how difficult it is to drawl when everyone around you is speaking lickety-split. If everyone else slows down, you can slow down. And the reaction is automatic.

The chances of establishing an automatic stutter-free rate are much better when children are preschoolers than after they start school. For preschoolers, the family is the model. There is vastly more leverage available to change a family than to change peer pressure at school.

Having said this, the task for the family is still enormous. One's speaking rate does not exist in isolation. It reflects a life style, how fast you gesture, how fast you

*During infancy, parents are his world. You only have to respond when your baby wants you to respond.*

*Even if parents did
all the right
things—picking
their infants up,
kissing, cuddling,
cooing and all the
rest—but often
ignored their
children's requests
for such attention,
then unlimited love
under that
condition would not
teach them that
they can obtain
affection when they
need it.*

walk, how fast you perform daily chores, how tightly you schedule your time, how much you overload yourself, how tolerant you are, how irritable you are. The list goes on and on. It is virtually impossible to permanently change one thing without changing everything else.

So the question, "How do we do it?" is not worth considering until you have answered the fundamental questions, "How badly do we want to do it?" and "Can we do it?" Put bluntly, you must decide whether preventing your child from stuttering is worth changing your family's lifestyle. The more you want to say "yes," the harder you will try, and the higher the price will be. But the reward will be worth it.

*School Children*

If your child is of school age, the foregoing suggestions are still applicable and important, but their effectiveness will probably need to be supplemented. If he has stuttered for several years, he may need to learn fluency skills with which to free him from the disruptions of stuttering. Once he has stuttered long enough for it to become automatic, he risks losing the feel of what it is like to speak without stuttering. A speech clinician who has experience working with children who stutter will probably be needed to help him learn the necessary skills for the feeling of fluency.

A word of admonition. Learning how to use fluency skills requires concentrated attention before easy speech will ever become automatic. These skills involve comfortably slow easy speech. His chances of maintaining easy speech until it becomes automatic are virtually nil if he comes home to a family of fast talkers each day after school. If easy speech does not become automatic, the drudgery of thinking about the skills needed to maintain fluency will soon wear thin. Stuttering will become the lesser of the two evils. When a constitutional predisposition to stutter is the underlying cause of disruption, the probability of being able to talk faster eventually is slim. To have a family which models easy speech is, therefore, essential if a lifetime of stuttering is to be prevented.

*The foundation of security is the child's knowledge that he can control his world.*

# Section IV:
# Stutterer Prevented

*Who does not crave being cared for just because you are you, not for what you've done or the affection you've earned for being "good"?*

# Stutterer Characteristics

Continuing to stutter after childhood and *becoming* a stutterer are two very different matters. Most everyone stutters, one way or another, but few of us even recognize it. Only those who build their lives around stuttering as a means of coping with speaking situations in which they have lost control will come to think of themselves as stutterers, even though they do not like to be called stutterers.

*Who does not crave being encouraged to talk—about themselves, about anything and everything?*

Children who are more likely to become stutterers:

- have difficulty asserting themselves in entering and controlling conversations.
- have parents who pay attention mainly when they stutter.
- feel insecure.
- think of themselves as stutterers.
- feel timid or shy.
- feel frustrated or helpless when they stutter.
- tighten throat, mouth, or chest.
- avoid or substitute words when they expect to stutter.

*Children will learn that they can control their lives, which is the foundation of security, as they learn that they can incite anger as well as evoke love— when they need it.*

- have (in order of importance) a mother, grandmother, sister, aunt, father, grandfather, brother, or uncle who stuttered.
- feel hesitant to speak out.
- feel unsuccessful competing for attention.

A child does not have to have all of these conditions to become a stutterer, but he does have to have the first three. Any of the others can contribute, but the first three must be prevented if children who stutter are to be saved from having the problems of becoming stutterers. Here are the reasons why these conditions make children vulnerable.

## Descriptions

### *Difficulty with Assertiveness*

Difficulty getting into and controlling a conversation is the soil in which pay-offs of stuttering flourish. When children have this difficulty, the conversation goes over, around, by, and through them as if they did not exist. As adults, this situation is painful enough. There is no reason to think that it is any less painful for children. It hurts when those who ignore them are important to them, especially when it is their own parents.

SUMMARY: DIFFICULTY CONTROLLING CONVERSATIONS IS A PREREQUISITE FOR BECOMING A STUTTERER.

### *Attention when Stuttering*

Another prerequisite is to have a parent who pays little attention to what the child says except when he stutters. Not that the attention then is likely to be pleasant. It's more likely to be a reprimand: "Stop that," "Slow down," "Think before you speak." Sadly, reprimands are better than no attention. Because stuttering is required to get a response, stuttering is what receives the pay-off. Children don't know that this is what is happening, but this is how everyone learns things they don't even know they're learning.

The doubly unfortunate part is that both being ignored and being reprimanded breed resentment. But how is a child supposed to express resentment to a parent who won't listen to him in the first place and whose affection he needs? When stuttering gains needed attention (such as it may be), probably mixed with concern, then why risk open resentment? Not that a child figures this out and does it on purpose. Stuttering would not occur if that were the case. No, even adults learn this sort of thing without even realizing they ever learned it.

*With security comes reduced risk of stuttering.*

SUMMARY: A PARENT WHO RESPONDS MORE WHEN STUTTERING OCCURS, THAN WHEN THE CHILD TRIES FOR ATTENTION BY TALKING, PROVIDES A CRITICAL PREREQUISITE FOR BECOMING A STUTTERER.

*Set realistic expectations. If they are too low, there is no challenge. If too high, the risk of failure is too great. When the challenge is just right, accomplishing it is exhilarating.*

## Insecurity

When children feel uneasy about asserting themselves, they have the basis for the lifelong problems of stutterers. These problems are rooted in insecurity, which, for whatever reason, reflects the unavailability of parents when an infant needs them.

If babies cannot develop their sense of self-worth in the real world of responsive parenting, then they have no alternative but to develop fantasies of their worthiness. Without a sense of worth, real or fantasized, there can be no sense of self. Without a self there is no "I" to observe the world. Without observations of one's world, there would be nothing to talk about, and one cannot have disrupted speech without talking. Stuttering, then is an affirmation of one's sense of self-worth.

For this sense to develop in reality may require major changes in the lives of the family if stuttering is to be stopped in early childhood. When this sense has been established with unspoken fantasies, though, they are all but impervious to alteration in later years. The longer children rely on their fantasies, and the longer they rely on stuttering to protect them while being secretly assertive, the deeper the roots of both fantasies and stuttering become.

Fantasies are not subject to real life checks and validations. In them, one can be as powerful, noble, and perfect as one wishes with no dispute. Little wonder, then, that they typically fuel dominance conflicts. How can people not be in conflict when those in real life treat them like flawed real people, not like they see themselves in their fantasies? By the time the person who stutters has be-come a stutterer, the task of trading insecurity of a fantasy for the abrasions of reality is profoundly difficult and requires extraordinary strength.

**SUMMARY: INSECURITY IS THE UNDERLYING PREREQUISITE FOR DIFFICULTIES WITH ASSERTIVENESS AND VULNERABILITY TO THE ADDICTIVE POWER OF PAY-OFFS FOR STUTTERING.**

*A challenge has to have some risk of failure if meeting it is to be exhilarating. The probability of success, however, must outweigh the risk.*

### Self-Image of the Stutterer

One of the surest signs that stuttering has become an habitual method of coping with assertiveness needs is when speakers think of themselves as stutterers. Usually this does not happen until at least adolescence. For some it has not become much of a problem until peer pressure enters their lives with a vengeance. Then, too, it takes a while for the pay-offs of stuttering to become addictive. When they do, people who stutter then build their lives around the image of themselves as stutterers. In this image, speech is seen as a source of power; if they didn't stutter, they would be able to use that power. But since they do stutter, it protects them from having to test it in the real world. Thus, when children show signs of thinking of themselves as stutterers, they have taken a major step toward making their stuttering permanent.

*Until speech develops, babies only have a signal system, but it is an ancient one, tested in the crucible of evolution. If they cannot succeed with it, then the foundation on which speech will be built will be shaky.*

## SUMMARY: THE IMAGE OF "STUTTERER" MAKES STUTTERING ESSENTIAL TO THE SELF-CONCEPT.

### Shyness

Shy, timid children can be as secure as if they were born assertive. One does not have to be hail-fellow-well-met to be secure, or to not stutter. Timid children can be so secure in themselves and their private interests that they do not want to command attention. Nonetheless, a potential problem with being inherently shy is that one is likely to be imposed on or ignored. This is more apt to be troubling to shy children if they are also insecure. Being insecure means that they may be trying to cope by using fantasies with which to feel important, perfect, powerful. Being timid means that they are likely to shy away from speaking out. Put this combination together in situations in which children feel slighted and the probability of a dominance conflict, so important to stuttering, can be fueled. Shutting off this fuel supply by fostering confidence and assertiveness is essential if stuttering is to be stopped.

## SUMMARY: SHYNESS INCREASES ANY TENDENCY TOWARD INSECURITY.

### Frustration or Helplessness

When children stutter and feel either frustrated or helpless, these are almost certain signs that they are being disrupted for reasons they cannot control. Loss of control goes beyond speech; it extends to communication, and even one's identity. Loss of control and the child's inability to prevent it is the essence of what chronic stuttering becomes. It contributes to the protection of the stutterer self-image. It is as if stutterers say to themselves, "If I cannot prevent stuttering, no matter how hard I try, then how can anyone possibly know how great a speaker I could be?"

**SUMMARY: HELPLESSNESS TO PREVENT STUTTERING PRESERVES ITS POWER TO PROTECT A STUTTERER'S SELF-IMAGE.**

*As growing children, they will carry the burden of trying to disprove that their earliest conviction is false: that they are not worthy enough to command attention. Their life, then, will begin on a premise of insecurity.*

### *Throat, Mouth, or Chest Tightening*

Tightening of throat, mouth, or chest when about to stutter results from a conflict about assertiveness. It does not seem to occur with other causes of stuttering. It could be a reflexive response to holding back on resentment about losing control of a speaking situation. It could be a reflexive response to fear of speaking out. As Herbert Goldberg (who is about as close to being a cured stutterer as I know) says, "The adult stutterer knows . . . that he is really not in great jeopardy at the moment that he is unable to introduce himself to a stranger . . . . However, as a child, he was really afraid in such a situation and the fear persists, causing high tension levels." Whatever the

*Obviously, the best chance for prevention is in infancy.*

cause, the greater the fear of holding back, the greater the tension. It is this tension which tells the speaker he is going to stutter. It could also be the direct cause of loss of control which, because it apparently is reflexive, cannot be prevented. Or, it could cause stuttering. Either way, it results in loss of control.

**SUMMARY: TIGHTENING OF THROAT, MOUTH, OR CHEST SEEMS TO BE A CLEAR SIGN THAT THE CAUSE OF STUTTERING IS A CONFLICT OVER CONTROL OF SPEAKING SITUATIONS.**

### Avoidance and Substitution

Avoidance and substitution of words follow expectancy to stutter on them. This goes for avoidance of feared situations and persons as well. Expectancy to stutter goes hand in glove with tightening of throat, mouth, or chest. Admittedly, substituting can have a rosy effect, although I know of only one such instance. Physician and performing artist Jonathan Miller, perhaps the most articulate and fluent speaker I've ever heard, was asked once by TV host Dick Cavett how he had developed such a huge vocabulary. I was astounded to hear Miller say that he stuttered, but hated to be heard doing it. As a consequence, he had acquired a large vocabulary with which to weave his way around any impending stuttering. For mere mortals who stutter, however, avoiding and substituting are the kiss of death. They can monstrify what could be a relatively minor stuttering problem. They add to the vicious circle of stuttering. The more that difficult words or situations are avoided, the more fearful they become, so the more they have to be avoided. Avoidance, with its cousin, substitution, is a major fuel for preserving helplessness to prevent stuttering.

**SUMMARY: AVOIDANCE AND SUBSTITUTION PRESERVE STUTTERING BY PRESERVING THE FEELING OF HELPLESSNESS TO PREVENT IT.**

*If parents could act to prevent failed efforts to communicate successfully before speech appears, let alone stuttering, then inherently dangerous conflict-driven stuttering would not begin in the first place.*

### Has Relative Who Stutters

Even if you were an identical twin and your brother stuttered, you would not be foreordained to stutter. Admittedly, the probability would be high. One study has the risk at 77 percent if you were identical twins and at 32 percent if you were fraternal. The overall estimate, when stuttering runs in a family, is that the risk is about three times greater than if it did not. Moreover, if stuttering is on the maternal side (a mother, grandmother, sister, or aunt), as it was with Sue, the risk is greater than if it is on the father's side. The reason is because stuttering, like height, is a male characteristic. It takes more genetic power to produce stuttering, or height, in girls than in boys. Hence, more boys, or girls, in a family are likely to stutter if the mother stutters than if the father stutters.

*What we will consider first is what can be done to minimize, if not stop, stuttering that is relatively harmless. This is the stuttering that may be of more concern to you than to your child.*

Having said all of this, no one really understands how stuttering is transmitted genetically. We are reasonably certain, though, that it can be. We are even more certain that by itself, heredity does not produce stuttering. It can contribute, however, in several ways. The most direct effect is to limit the speed with which the components of speech can be coordinated. Whenever this limit is exceeded, stuttering would result. When such children are insecure, the probability is great of the pay-offs for their frequent stuttering becoming addictive.

The effect can also be more indirect. Heredity can affect how easily a child masters spoken language. Uncertainty about word selection, pronunciation, correct grammar can make for stuttering disruptions. Such stuttering, however, is likely to be outgrown by puberty when language matures, but not always.

Finally, children tend to be born with a temperament ranging from assertive to timid. Those tending to be timid will not be naturally inclined to be assertive. They are more apt to be vulnerable to stuttering and its pay-offs.

**SUMMARY: HEREDITY CAN CONTRIBUTE TO STUTTERING BY INCREASING THE PROBABILITY OF SPEECH DISRUPTIONS. IN ADDITION, BEING BORN WITH A TIMID TEMPERAMENT CAN CONTRIBUTE TO BECOMING A STUTTERER.**

## Hesitant to Speak Out

Children who are hesitant or fearful of speaking are obviously insecure about speaking out. Combine the insecure power fantasy with not feeling free to speak out with the option of lapsing into resentful silence, or of pushing into conversation under time pressure, and you have another manifestation of the assertiveness conflict which fuels lifelong stuttering.

**SUMMARY: HESITATION TO SPEAK OUT HELPS PRESERVE HELPLESSNESS TO PREVENT STUTTERING.**

*Children most likely to outgrow stuttering with which you may be concerned are disrupted for reasons they can be aware of, in particular, linguistic stuttering.*

## Unsuccessful in Competition

The only area in which stutterers necessarily have trouble competing is speech. Many of the world's great leaders have been stutterers: Moses, Aristotle, Newton, Darwin, Churchill. Still, success in any area helps reduce the need for stuttering. On the other hand, inability to easily control speaking situations contributes to stuttering. It is because of unsuccessful attempts to control conversations and parental attention that stuttering developed in the first place. Any form of success is, of course, helpful, especially if it involves speaking.

**SUMMARY: SUCCESS IN COMPETITION HELPS REDUCE THE NEED FOR STUTTERING.**

*Children who are confident, secure, and assertive, who are not selective about where or with whom they stutter, who like to talk, speak out without hesitation, compete success-fully, and pay little attention to whatever stutter-ing may occur, are the children most likely to outgrow it.*

# Guide to Strategies

Many of the characteristics we examined of children most likely to become stutterers are not easily observed. Having these characteristics does *not* automatically make them stutter or turn them into stutterers. A description is given for each strategy of things you can observe, if your child does stutter, which will give you a rather accurate idea of the problem he faces and of the strategy which would be of most help.

Section IV is intended to cope with three different possibilities. One is the child whose stuttering is due largely to continued uncertainty about pronunciation, word selection, proper grammar—any of these can result in frequent speech disruptions. The child is also so inse-cure that he struggles to enter conversations. The result is linguistic stuttering, which could eventually lead to be-coming a stutterer, but need not, depending on how many other contributing characteristics compound the prob-lem. Strategy 4 is designed to stop such stuttering before it increases in severity. Observable signs are:

- He has difficulty asserting himself in entering and controlling conversations.
- Stuttering occurs before he is certain of the word to be spoken, or how to say it.
- Stuttering occurs on "filler sounds," such as "uh, uh, uh," which are not sounds in the word eventu-ally spoken.
- Severity of stuttering depends on who the listener is.

- He does not have to be excited for stuttering to occur.
- Stuttering started a year or more after he began to talk.
- He has had difficulty learning to talk.

Strategy 5 is for the insecure child who shows at least the major characteristics for a lifetime of stuttering who has not yet discovered the pay-offs which would lead to his becoming a stutterer. The objective is to stop this stuttering before it becomes addictive. Observable signs are:

*We have two objectives. The obvious one is to minimize stuttering, and to stop it in so far as possible. By far and away the most important objective, though, is to prevent it, for whatever reasons, from acquiring pay-offs.*

- He has difficulty asserting himself in entering and controlling conversations.
- Stuttering varies in frequency and severity from person to person.
- He does not stutter when alone.
- He stutters on words he is ready to say.
- Stuttering started developing a few years after connected speech began.
- He avoids or substitutes words when he expects to stutter.
- His throat and chest tighten when he stutters.

Strategy 6 is for the insecure child who has at least the three essential conditions for becoming a stutterer, which are:

- He has parents who pay attention mainly when he stutters.

*When pay-offs become an important tool for coping with assertiveness, then the person who had been stuttering has become a stutterer.*

- He has difficulty asserting himself in entering and controlling conversations.
- He is insecure.

He may also have any of the other characteristics described earlier of children most apt to become stutterers, but many of these are not readily observable. The two which you may be able to detect directly, and that your child can probably recognize, are:

- His throat, mouth, or chest tighten when he stutters.
- He avoids or substitutes words when he expects to stutter.

If you observe either of these two conditions along with the first two, then Strategy 6 is definitely the one to use.

## Stutterer Prevention Strategies

### Strategy 4: Stop Linguistic Stuttering

*Example*

Sally, who is Diane's (Strategy 2) and Ted's (Strategy 3) mother, had been a little girl who was much less interested in dolls than in competing with her brother. In truth, she was a feminine fast-talking tomboy who had been slow learning to talk. Her parents had been concerned enough to have a language therapist try to help her improve. By her fifth birthday, she had been having help for two years. By then, her remaining difficulty was pronouncing the sounds "r," "s," and "l."

During these years, her parents had tried to help the therapy along by correcting her errors in grammar, pronunciation, and articulation of her difficult sounds. The unintentional effect on Sally was to make her quite ambivalent about speech. On one hand, she was a competitor, so she tried to use the biggest words she had learned. Unfortunately, they were often the wrong words, and they were frequently mispronounced. This added to the opportunities for brother as well as parents to correct her. By the time Sally started school, her confidence in being able to speak out without risk of correction was pretty well undermined. It was when she had to read aloud in class that stuttering began. Some of her classmates had snickered when she made mistakes the first few times she read. By the end of a week, Sally stuttered each time she read. Then it spread to her home. She eventually could hardly talk with any of her family without stuttering. Still trying to help, they advised her to slow down, which only infuriated her.

Stuttering persisted all the way into high school. Her confidence began to grow, however, when she discovered she was good enough to sing solos. She tried out for plays, and graduated from small parts to leading parts. She still stuttered, but never on stage. In college, she decided to add debate to her singing and acting. She was apprehensive about it, but used it as a test of her courage. To her delight, she not only didn't stutter, she turned out to be good at it. Being a natural competitor, debating was right up her alley. After winning a major championship, she

*When we talk about preventing stuttering from becoming permanent, we will not be trying to prevent natural speech disruptions. That would be impossible to begin with, and the result would be unnatural if we succeeded.*

*Being fluent without exception may be desirable for TV announcers who are reading teleprompters, but in normal conversation, perfect fluency is almost freakish.*

said to herself the next day, "I'm not going to stutter. I don't need it any more." She didn't, and she hasn't since. She is now 39, is an attorney, has the family you have met and is still a fast-talking competitor.

## Procedure

Step 1. Listen carefully to what your child says, rather than to the way he says it. Repeating or rephrasing what you think he said is evidence to him that you listened.

Step 2. Observe whether you or other members of the family talk to him with big words or long complex sentences. If so, simplify your language, especially if he is a preschooler, and see if communication becomes easier.

Step 3. You would probably be wise to forego attempts to correct any speech problem until stuttering ceases to be a concern. Other speech and language problems, of course, are important, and may need professional attention. The difficulty with providing that attention when stuttering is still a problem is that any correcting can fuel an assertiveness conflict. If your child is already in therapy, then observe its effects on stuttering. If it increases, the therapy should probably be postponed until the difficulties of stuttering have been resolved.

Step 4. (Preschool)  If your child is not disturbed by his interruptions, do not call his attention to them or show signs of concern. If he is disturbed, tell him the truth—that everyone has some trouble talking from time to time. Do not give him instruction as to what he should do to not stutter. Telling him to slow down puts him under pressure, which you need to lower, not raise. Anyway, slowing down would be of little help for the Strategy 4 condition.

**Strategy 1** *is for children who have a good chance of outgrowing their stuttering without much help.*

Step 4. (Older child)  If he is not disturbed by his interruptions, do not make a problem where none exists. Treat disruptions as casually as if he were speaking normally, which may be the case. The steps which follow are for older children who are disturbed by their disruptions, and can understand what they can do to help themselves.

Step 5. If your child resents being corrected by you or other members of the family, use the services of a speech clinician to implement the steps that follow. If he is not resentful, you may use these steps at home.

Step 6. When he repeats or is blocked on a sound, such as "uh," that is not part of the word he eventually speaks, then ask casually if he knew the word he was trying to say when you heard "uh."

Step 7. Without making a big thing of it, help him to see the connection between the "filler sounds" he makes and his searching for a word, or a way of phrasing his idea. This will not necessarily reduce the disruptions. Instead, *it is intended to reduce his concern* about them.

*In addition to the vast majority of children who stutter for a while and then outgrow it, a small group will continue who can be helped with Strategies 2 or 3.*

Assuming your child is receptive to your help, listen carefully to his stuttering. Make recordings of it so that you can study it without intruding on him any more than necessary. What you need to determine is whether he is stuttering on a word he is prepared to say. If the sound he repeats or is blocked on does not belong to the word he speaks after the stuttering stops, then ask, as if it were merely a matter of idle curiosity, if he knew the word he wanted to say before he stuttered. You will probably have to find ways of tailoring this inquiry to fit his understanding of what you are asking.

Your purpose, of course, is to help him see that he is disrupted by his attempts to talk before he has selected he word he wants to say next. This insight gives him potential control over the disruptions, because he then knows that he has the option of stopping and figuring out what he wants to say instead of being disrupted. The potential frustration and helplessness of stuttering are thereby removed.

Because the driving force behind time pressure, in this instance, is an assertiveness conflict, you may or may not need the help of a speech clinician to accomplish the foregoing objective. If your efforts to help your child in other ways have been met with resentment, then use a speech clinician. The risk you would run otherwise would be his feeling that you were requiring him to do something "for his own good," which in his mind could easily translate into being forced to do it for your good.

Persistence of the disruptions do not necessarily indicate that your efforts have failed. The important clues for concern, however, are whether or not he shows signs of conflict or of reacting to stuttering. Tensing of throat, mouth, or chest when stuttering is a major clue. So is avoidance. It can take such forms as substituting words or avoiding troublesome situations. Any signs of fear or frustration also indicate the need for professional help.

Linguistic uncertainty contributes to stuttering, when exuberance is not the cause, only when lack of confidence impairs feeling free to speak out. Given linguistic uncertainty, reducing its effects is by far the easiest route to prevention. As a cause of stuttering, it is readily available to the awareness of children old enough to understand cause and effect. Uncertainty about how to phrase an idea, about word selection, or about pronunciation are normally resolved by thinking about the solution. But speech is typically produced automatically. When time pressure to continue a statement or to jump into a conversation is high, children can try to talk even when they do not know the word they are trying to say.

Remember, too, that speech disruptions are normal occurrences. They become stuttering when their cause is unknown. That is what breeds the feeling of helplessness and loss of control. The objective for older children, then, can be prevention of loss of control rather than of the disruption itself, which can happen to anyone. This can be done by raising awareness of the cause of the disruption.

**Strategy 2** *is for children who can recover who have stuttered for more than a year.*

**Strategy 3** *is designed to help children who stutter when outside pressure is applied.*

## Strategy 5: Stop Assertiveness-Conflict Stuttering

### *Example*

We met Billy earlier (p. 26). It was Billy whose older brother taunted him by butting into dinner conversations whenever he tried to talk. Billy soon began to stutter under the pressure. As you might suspect, there was more to this story than that. Shortly before Billy was two, his bully brother caught an infection that quickly inflamed his throat so much he couldn't breathe. By the time medical help opened his windpipe enough for him to get air, he had turned blue and his heart had stopped. When revived, he went into convulsions and was hospitalized.

During the brother's illness, Billy was farmed out to friends for a month. Before, he had been an outgoing independent child. When he came home, he clung to his mother for a week. He was now easily frustrated and angered. His brother had become the focus of attention and was not about to relinquish it as Billy started becoming more active as he grew older. Despite resenting being bullied, his brother had become Billy's idol. Whatever he did, Billy tried to do.

The situation became compounded when Billy's parents began punishing his brother. The more the mother pursued the brother to leave Billy alone, the more the brother retaliated with merciless teasing. It was at this point that the stuttering started. Initially, it was only when the brother was around. Within a month it had spread to conversations with his parents. By age four he often stuttered severely.

The quarrels and conflicts persisted until the summer before Billy was to start school. Fortunately, the brother had been waging a campaign to visit a cousin who had horses, so he was given his wish to spend the entire summer vacation on the farm. Billy, who had wanted to go along, was now brought into the parent's vacation planning conference. They pored over travel brochures until they found a ranch with horses operated by a cowboy star whose TV show Billy watched avidly.

That summer was Billy's salvation. He was king of the mount, literally. He met his TV hero, and even rode his horse. The other cowboys at the ranch were his pals. He called them by their first names. His parents treated him as if he were the most important person in the world, which he was during that vacation. By the second week, the stuttering had all but disappeared.

The vacation ended a month before the brother came home. During those weeks, the parents made a concerted effort to preserve Billy's new-found sense of confidence. Except once when Billy got out of line and was punished, stuttering did not reappear.

Then came the critical test—the brother came home from the farm. Some preliminary sparring began, but the brother was too full of his summer's adventures to pay much attention to Billy. That evening everyone listened attentively to those adventures. Then it was Billy's turn. When he revealed that he not only knew their cowboy

*If your child shows signs of disturbance when disrupted, be calmly honest; openly acknowledge the difficulty he is having without making it a big thing.*

*We must assume that children who fit Strategy 3 are secure within themselves. Given that assumption, the major problem which can arise, and be altered, is within the family. It is the problem of the family's effect on a child's habitual speaking rate.*

hero—the brother's favorite as well as Billy's—the brother was so full of questions that his bullying didn't have a chance to revive. With both boys off to school, it didn't surface again as a serious problem. Neither did the stuttering. Without that summer, Billy could, and possibly would, have stuttered for life.

## Procedure

Apply the Golden Rule by asking yourself, what could be done to you that would leave you feeling "put down"? This step defines what everyone associated with your child should be alert for. This concern will run through all aspects of this prevention strategy. The following steps are examples of what you can do to minimize his feeling of being put down. The objective is to reduce the conditions which contribute to his feeling that he is being seen as subordinate in the real world, while also reducing his temptation to get special treatment because of his stuttering.

Step 1. Determine as objectively as you can how you interact with your child. You could use an interaction analysis form, as follows:

### Interaction Analysis Form

Keep a record of your interaction by making strokes like this, ‖‖, for each question, after each hour or after each occurrence. Do not delay in recording an occurrence.

A.   How many hours did you spend with
     your child today?                               _____

B.  How many times did he want your attention?  _____

C.  How many of these times did you hold him, play with him or listen to him attentively?  _____

D.  How many times did you do any of these things when he did not seek your attention?  _____

E.  How many times did he frustrate you?  _____

F.  How many times did you hide your frustration, annoyance, or anger?  _____

G.  How many times did you express these feelings openly, (by yelling or spanking, for example?)  _____

*The temptation for the family to admonish the child to "slow down" will be received as a power play of the worst order. It is a "do as I say, not as I do" admonition to be avoided at all times.*

Step 2. Use scores for each question to improve responsiveness to your child. Following are recommendations for improvement, question by question.

A.  If your A score is low (less than 2 or 3 hours) for this question, it may be because you work and your child is in nursery school. The question then is, "Does he look forward to nursery school each day?" If yes, then no problem. If no, then it may be adding to his sense of failure rather than success. This gets to the fundamental purpose of this strategy—improve his sense of security by improving his sense of success when interacting with family and playmates.

**Strategy 4 *is designed to stop linguistic stuttering before it increases in severity.***

Remember that stuttering caused by an assertiveness conflict is direct testimony to not feeling privileged to speak out. This feeling is a statement of insecurity. Young children will feel successful, hence improve their security, to the extent that they are successful in controlling the responsiveness of their family, especially their parents, and their playmates.

Although the role of parents diminishes, especially through the school years, it nonetheless is by far the most vital relationship during preschool years. When assertiveness-conflict stuttering appears during those years, the possibility of successful prevention falls squarely on them.

Thus, if your child does not like nursery school, the only potentially successful prevention strategy is to increase the number of hours of successful parenting at home. Of course, this recommendation is doubly important if you are at home all day, but do not spend much time with him.

B/C/D. Compare the number of times your child requested your attention (score B) with the number of times you responded with interest and affection (score C) to obtain a measure of how much success your child experienced in managing his most important relationship. Now compare your score for C with your score for D. Ideally, D would be zero. Although D does provide attention and affection, he has no control over when it happens. The higher

D is, relative to C, the more your child is learning that he has little, if any, ability to manage important relationships. This lesson paves the road to a basic sense of insecurity.

E/F/G. Compare the number of times he frustrated or angered you (E) with scores F and G.  If your F score is close to or higher than your G score, then you are probably contributing to his feeling of insecurity. Not only does he need to see honest affection and interest, he also needs to see honest evidence of irritation and anger. By hiding negative feelings, he is shown only a positive response to anything he does. He can detect underlying feelings of irritation or anger peeking out around the edges of attempts to mask them. Accordingly, if you tell him you are not irritated when he feels you are, then he will not only learn to  distrust what you tell him about your negative feelings, but also what you tell him about your positive feelings. He is also learning another equally important lesson when attempts are made to hide feelings. He is being told that he is too weak to be treated as a fully capable member of the family. Hiding feelings from him says implicitly that he has to be protected. Obviously, he can never gain strength or security from that sort of treatment.

Step 3. Continue this interaction analysis until your C scores have been raised high enough to ensure an adequate increase in your child's potential interaction successes. Increased scores only provide

*A child's chances of maintaining easy speech until it becomes automatic are virtually nil if he comes home to a family of fast talkers each day after school.*

**Strategy 5** *is for the insecure child who has not yet discovered the pay-offs of becoming a stutterer.*

increased opportunities. Whether these opportunities will count as successes will depend on raising C scores well above D scores, and G scores well above F scores.

Step 4. If you have accomplished Step 3 and have not seen distinct improvement in your child's speech in at least six months, then either the wrong prevention strategy is being used, or he is in need of a therapist to help him cope with feelings he is unable to expose within the family. If this is the case, then family therapy may also be needed.

## Strategy 6: Prevent Addictive Pay-Offs

There are several reasons to stutter, but only conflict over control of communication is the root cause of becoming a stutterer. Heredity and linguistic uncertainty often lead to stuttering and increase the opportunity for pay-offs. Only when they operate in conjunction with conflict over asserting oneself do they contribute to being a stutterer. Children who are secure and able to control communication are able to get attention when they need it. Such attention is usually pleasant, so the painful pay-offs of stuttering are of little value. But when those pay-offs are all the attention a child can obtain, then they pave the road to building one's life around the concept, "I am a stutterer."

### Example

George cannot remember when he didn't stutter. His parents told him it started as soon as he began to talk, a sign of a genetic cause. They had feared it would happen because stuttering ran in the family—George's father and grandfather both stuttered. You have already met some of George's family. His son, Ted, and daughter, Diane, inherited his predisposition to stutter, but are coping with it reasonably well since conflict does not seem to be a factor for either, especially for Diane. As you may recall, conflict was the major factor in his wife Sally's stuttering when she was growing up.

*Stuttering caused by an assertiveness conflict is direct testimony to not feeling privileged to speak out. This feeling is a statement of insecurity.*

George is now a very bright, laid back executive. Even though many of his colleagues do not know he stutters, he knows it. He still thinks of himself as a stutterer. The feelings of being at risk of stuttering are still there.

He was the middle brother who had to fight for everything. The problem was that he was a quiet baby and a quiet little boy. Unlike his brothers, who loved to fight, he hated it. He always had his nose buried in a book. When he did talk, he stuttered severely, which was occasion for his brothers to tease him. His parents didn't pay much attention to him, although they always told him they loved him. From George's point of view, they didn't act like it. The only time he remembers getting them to respond was when he stuttered, and then it was unpleasant. They scolded him for it, got upset, told him to slow down, and generally treated him as if he had done it on purpose.

George had therapy all the way through school, but it didn't help much. It was when Ted began to stutter that George decided to get help for himself again, this time from a clinic that specialized in treatment of stuttering with fluency skills.

*Young children will feel successful, hence improve their security, to the extent that they are successful in controlling the responsiveness of their family, especially their parents, and their playmates.*

Because George had stuttered from the time he started talking, and stuttered when alone if he read aloud rapidly, the diagnostic implication was that a genetic cause existed. The fact that his father and grandfather stuttered also indicated that he had probably inherited a constitutional basis for stuttering.

There was more to it than that, however. He was full of fears and avoidances. Some people he could talk with easily; others tied him up terribly. This was not a sign of a genetic cause, it was a sign of an assertiveness conflict. Considering how shy he had been as a boy and how aggressive his brothers had been, such a conflict was not surprising. He continues to stutter more with them than anyone else, and is still especially shy around them. Add to this the annoyance of linguistic uncertainty as a minor contributor to his stuttering. Evidence of this is seen when he occasionally stutters when he doesn't know the word he is trying to say.

Taken together at the time he was growing up, life-long stuttering was virtually foreordained for him from childhood. Back then, no one knew the causes of stuttering, nor what could be done about them. Not that this combination of causes is unusual. It is a combination found frequently among stutterers. By using fluency skills, he learned how to sound like a normal speaker, but he certainly didn't *feel* like one. He clung to the hope he started with, that these skills would eventually become automatic so that he wouldn't have to think about them. It was this hope that drove him to attend therapy sessions designed to maintain fluency skills. But his doubts were growing that controlled fluency would ever become so automatic that he could speak spontaneously.

Then one session, his clinician challenged him to choose one of the situations he habitually avoided. The idea was for him to use his fluency skills when he entered that situation. Then, when he felt confident that he could cope, he was to switch from controlled speech to spontaneous speech. This meant that he would put himself at risk of stuttering, which was why he avoided the situation in the first place.

George accepted the challenge, chose a situation he thought he could handle, and had such an exhilarating success that he decided to take a giant leap to the most fearful situation he avoided. His reason was that he thought that if he could face up to his worst avoidance, then he would no longer fear any of the lesser ones.

It didn't work out that way, but not because he failed. In truth, he tried his toughest one and succeeded. The problem was that the challenge he set for himself was too big. The fact that he succeeded struck him as being pure luck.

What he then did was to go back to his list of avoidances, rank them in order of difficulty, and take them one at a time, starting with the easiest. By using his fluency skills to establish his confidence when entering each situation, he could then speak out spontaneously. Even though he sometimes stuttered, he could still feel in control of his successes.

Stuttering has become a manageable problem for George. Most who think of themselves as stutterers do

*Not only does he need to see honest affection and interest, he also needs to see honest evidence of irritation and anger.*

*Hiding feelings from him says implicitly that he has to be protected.*

not do as well. George doesn't stutter much anymore, but he doesn't try to hide it much either. If he continues to face up to it openly, the day may come when he doesn't have to think about it at all. He may end up not thinking of himself as a stutterer. Until then, it will remain a problem to be dealt with day in and day out.

## General Strategy

The key to preventing your child from becoming a stutterer is how you respond to him. If you are interested in what he does and what he has to say, your interest will usually be apparent to him in many subtle, as well as obvious, ways. It is difficult to fake genuine interest. Still, there are so many legitimate distractions: getting dinner ready, household chores, taking care of a baby, being tired after a day's work, relaxing with TV or a newspaper —the list is endless. The distraction of a child trying to get your attention can often be frustrating to say the least.

The damage occurs when you are so preoccupied that you don't pay attention to what he is doing or saying —until he stutters. If that grabs your attention more than anything else he does, then you have sent him a strong signal about how to get your attention. He doesn't know he is learning a lesson. Fortunately, it generally takes years to learn it. Once learned, he will never forget it. As the adage goes, "once a stutterer, always a stutterer." You can prevent that adage from coming true.

### Preschool Children

This is the age at which prevention possibilities are greatest. No one but parents are heavily involved in the solution. Children struggling for attention more or less expect brothers and sisters to taunt and tease. But parents are the Rock of Gibraltar. Who else can be expected to be there when needed if not them? When a child who fits the characteristics of Strategy 6 stutters, he is announcing to you that his straightforward methods of getting your interest have not succeeded. He is saying that the particular situation in which he stutters is his last resort for gaining attention. *He does not do this on purpose.* He does not want to stutter. If you are concerned with preventing the problem from becoming permanent, heed his message from the time you first hear it.

**Strategy 6** *is for the insecure child in conflict over freedom to be assertive.*

## *Procedure*

Step 1. When your child stutters, ask yourself these questions to guide you in analyzing what you were doing before he stuttered, and how you responded to his stuttering.

> A. Was I listening to what he was saying or watching what he was doing with enthusiastic interest, or was my attention elsewhere?
>
> B. If I was doing something else, why didn't I pay attention to him?
>
> C. When he stuttered, did that get my attention?
>
> > Did I then listen attentively?
> >
> > Did I try to correct him?
> >
> > Was I calm or upset?

Step 2. Consider how you would like to react next time.

> Note that if you paid special attention to him

*Children who are secure and able to control communication are able to get attention when they need it. Such attention is usually pleasant, so the painful pay-offs of stuttering are of little value.*

when he stuttered, none of your responses were helpful. If you were upset and corrected him, he got attention, even if it was unpleasant. If you were calm and listened attentively, he got the kind of attention he could really enjoy, but he got it for stuttering.

Step 3. Recognize that your only helpful attention will be to attend to what he has to say and to what he is doing which does not involve stuttering.

Step 4. Provide this attention when he indicates he wants it. You can assume that whenever he talks to you he wants it. Avoid providing it when he is talking to himself, or is preoccupied with what he is doing. It is important to be responsive, not intrusive.

Step 5. If you have trouble carrying out any of these four steps, consult a speech clinician who has experience with young children who stutter.

This foregoing procedure is similar to an activity which Dr. Richard Mallard, who devised it, calls "Talk Time." It is presented in the Appendix, complete with verbatim transcripts of the interactions of the family of a four-year-old boy who stuttered. As you will see, it is an activity which can yield some powerful results.

*School Children*

Once in school the problem of minimizing pay-offs for stuttering becomes much more difficult, for obvious reasons. More people are involved (students, teachers), and their attention becomes increasingly important. Improving that attention will be difficult. The help of the teacher and the speech clinician at school may be essential.

There is also the additional pay-off of special privileges afforded by stuttering. The more severe stuttering is, the greater opportunity for privilege it affords. It can get him out of talking. It can get him out of chores. It can get him out of reciting at school. It can get him out of challenging social relationships. It can get him special favors. When he tries to cope in the real world, even if he fails frequently, he at least gains strength by rising repeatedly to daily challenges. When his stuttering is used for protection, each escape adds to his sense of weakness and insecurity. Although the family is not likely to be able to provide enough social successes to alter stuttering much at this age, lack of support can effectively undo gains made in therapy. The following steps can be used initially to determine how much can be achieved within the family. Even if these steps are not adequately successful by themselves, they nonetheless lay the foundation for what can be accomplished in child and family therapy.

To prevent conflict-caused stuttering from becoming permanent requires reducing children's insecurities. This is accomplished by demonstrating to them that they can be successful in controlling their sense of worth. By the time conflict-stuttering starts, they already will have been unsuccessful commanding attention as infants with their signal system and rudimentary speech. In other words, they are at risk of relying on fantasies for their feelings

*When pay-offs of stuttering are all the attention a child can obtain, then they pave the road to building one's life around the concept, "I am a stutterer."*

*The distraction of a child trying to get your attention can often be frustrating.*

of security. Once established, fantasies will be difficult for them to renounce. When people see themselves as stutterers a special difficulty is that the stuttering provides a reasonable explanation why in the real world they cannot be all that they are in their fantasies. This is why the "giant-in-chains" feeling often develops in those who become stutterers. It is a major source of addictiveness. Because their fantasies lead them into expectations of power that are not realized, fantasized assertiveness is in conflict with actual insecurity.

The only remaining opportunity children have at home to prove to themselves that they can succeed is in family conversations. The importance of this opportunity cannot be overstated. Although family influence continues into the school years, it becomes increasingly diluted as the importance of opinions of classmates and teachers increases. These are difficult to control. Hence, the importance of ensuring success at home when the opportunity arises.

**MARVIN** by Tom Armstrong

Reprinted with special permission of North America Syndicate, Inc.

The tactics needed to provide older children with the chance to maximize this opportunity require a keen sense of discretion. What needs to be demonstrated is that these children are just as important as anyone else, and that they can have as much impact on a conversation as anyone else, whether they stutter or whether they do not. Discretion is critical because any attempt to provide such opportunities can easily be seen as patronizing.

There is nothing that demeans and infuriates people who stutter more than being patronized. What that means to anyone, not just children who stutter, is that we think they cannot compete on equal footing, so they have to be extended special privileges, they have to be "treated with kid gloves." Because assertiveness-conflict stuttering is an explicit protest against just such treatment, to be patronized is the ultimate insult. Perhaps the most galling example for those who stutter is to have people "help" by completing words on which they are stuck. Strict avoidance of such "help" applies just as much to help from other children as from adults.

What this caution implies is that opportunities for communicative success must not be extended as charades. These opportunities must be honest expressions of how you feel. Herein lies the difficulty. People cannot just tell themselves to change and expect to feel differently. Change is a process. You may be able to do this alone or you may need the professional help of a speech therapist with experience in family counseling.

The problem to be resolved is why does your older child who stutters feel that he is not privileged to enter

*The damage occurs when you are so preoccupied that you don't pay attention to what he is doing or saying—until he stutters.*

*If stuttering grabs your attention more than anything else he does, then you have sent him a strong signal about how to get your attention.*

into family conversations on an equal footing? He may feel that he either has to fight his way into conversations, or give up trying because you and the family do not see him as being important enough to merit attention. Such feelings may be the residue of unfortunate parenting in his earliest years which was a consequence of uncontrollable circumstances. How he feels now may not reflect accurately how you felt then, or now. If he does misperceive how you and the others in your family truly feel about him, then the problem is his. To resolve it will probably require help.

On the other side, you and your family need to explore how you really do feel about each other. This is not an opportunity for placing blame. If anyone does, the purpose of what you are doing will be defeated. If you discover that your child's complaint is valid about how anyone really feels, then that person needs to dig deeper. Regardless of who needs help, the issue must be confronted openly. The process of such a confrontation in itself is a step toward freedom from stuttering. For your older child to face your family and openly reveal what is going on under the surface is, in itself, an act of strength and courage. It is with this type of communication that he can prove to himself that he has the power to make an impact.

### Procedure

Step 1. Establish an Honesty Hour once a week. All of the family should attend. Initially, this hour can be used to air grievances. These have an objective basis and are not too threatening to talk about. This should not become an attempt at psychotherapy in which uncovering deep motives is the objective. It is intended, instead to give members of the family a chance to be honest with each other. The objective for your child who stutters is to be able to say openly and assertively what he holds back when he stutters. This procedure must be done with care in which what you like about each other outweighs what you don't like. No one enjoys being criticized unless it is in a supportive context. If at all possible, engage a speech clinician with family counseling skills to meet with you. This can be a powerful tool for improvement, but it should not be continued without professional help if the negative begins to outweigh the positive. To get a sense of how this activity might proceed, read the section of "Talk Time" in the Appendix beginning with "Third Therapy Session."

Step 2.  Gradually work how you feel about each other into the discussions. Try to keep focused on specific things family members have done that give you the feeling you are talking about. Also talk about what you think other members feel about each other, and what they have done to give you reason to feel this way. Your child who stutters should not be the focus or the initial reason for the Honesty Hour. The reason can be improved family relations, which is an honest reason for starters. In truth, this should be the reason from

*Parents are the child's Rock of Gibraltar. Who else can be expected to be there when needed if not them?*

*When a child who fits the charac- teristics of Strategy 6 stutters, he is announcing to you that his straightforward methods of getting your interest have not succeeded.*

start to finish, with your child who stutters being only one participant on equal footing with everyone else. No one in the family (including parents) should be specially privileged during this hour.

Step 3. After members have begun talking about what others do that gives people a basis for feeling whatever is felt about them, your child's stuttering can become a topic for exploration. Questions such as those that follow may help him to understand the feelings that lie behind his stuttering.

- "Do you stutter more with some people than with others?"
- "Do you feel differently towards them than the people you do not stutter with?"
- "What do you feel toward the person you're speaking to at the time you stutter?"
- "What do you think that person feels towards you?"
- "Why do you think your throat, mouth, or chest tighten when you stutter?"
- "Do they tighten more when you stutter severely?"
- "Do they tighten when you hold back your anger?"

Never let the focus remain more on your child who stutters than on anyone else. He should never be given a basis for feeling that he is singled out for concern, or is the reason for the Honesty Hour.

Step 4. Ask your child who stutters if he would like to learn some fluency skills which would make it easier for him to speak. Find a speech clinician who could provide such therapy. Accept whatever decision your child makes. Remember that *fluency is not the objective of therapy*. This point cannot be stressed too much. Even accepting this point, you will be sorely tempted to think of maintaining fluency as the most important accomplishment. Nothing could be farther from the truth. If your child wishes to learn fluency skills, fine—PRO-VIDED he learns them to help him achieve confidence that he can speak spontaneously without hiding his stuttering. If he uses them for any other purpose, he is sacrificing communication on the altar of fluency. He cannot concentrate on what he is saying if he has to be preoccupied with fluency skills for how he says it.

Step 5. If progress is apparent in how your child feels and speaks at home, then the Relaxation Game of Strategy 3 could be introduced if it has been interesting and successful. The reason for it in this prevention strategy would be to provide a basis for bringing your child's friends into a situation in which he could compete with them successfully. There are two prerequisites for using the Relaxation Game. One is that your child be good enough at it to be rewardingly successful within

*He is saying that the particular situation in which he stutters, is his last resort for gaining attention.* **He does not do this on purpose.** *He does not want to stutter.*

*If you are concerned with preventing stuttering from becoming permanent, heed his message from the time you first hear it.*

the family. This means that he be good enough at it to enjoy playing it. The other prerequisite is that the game be enjoyable enough that his school friends would want to play it. This game could be continued as long as it contributes to your child's improvement.

## Stop Stuttering to Prevent Stutterer

Obviously, the more that stuttering can be stopped, the greater the chance of preventing development of a stutterer. All of the strategies are designed to stop stuttering: Strategy 3 is for hereditary stuttering, Strategy 4 is for linguistic stuttering, and Strategy 5 is for assertiveness-conflict stuttering. Any of these strategies which are appropriate can be used to considerable advantage in conjunction with Strategy 6.

# Section V: Professional Help

*To prevent conflict-caused stuttering from becoming permanent requires reducing children's insecurities. This is accomplished by demonstrating to them that they can be successful in controlling their sense of worth.*

# Types of Professional Help

Once the image of stutterer has been established, with stuttering to protect it, prevention is no longer a possibility. What can be accomplished, with professional help, though, is improvement to the extent that stuttering can be reduced to a manageable part of life. The prospect of stuttering will still remain, but will be far enough out of sight and out of mind that it will not be a major problem. Equally important, the image of being a stutterer can be all but eliminated.

This is what Aileen said some years after her therapy began. "Prior to therapy, I saw myself as a 'stutterer.' Today, I see myself as someone who stutters—but has so many other facets to my life. Perhaps that is the reason why I'm not so *fluent* all the time (I don't practice a lot; only when I need to). But I do believe I *communicate* a lot more. Others like me, and I like myself—a truly great revelation. The therapy that is done today is much better focused on *communication*, than when I first started, when the emphasis seemed to be on *fluency*. I got so wrapped up in the fluency part that communication wasn't really me. I also believe that in certain incidents, I

*When people see themselves as stutterers a special difficulty is that their stuttering provides a reasonable explanation why in the real world they cannot be all that they are in their fantasies.*

**137**

*There is nothing that demeans and infuriates people who stutter more than being patronized.*

intentionally use my stuttering as a buffer/barrier against authority figures (my mom; my boss). Stuttering is also a delaying tactic when I can't gather my thoughts quick enough."

Three sources of help are available to achieve such recovery:

1. Speech clinicians offer fluency, stuttering-management, and counseling therapies.
2. Clinical psychologists offer psychotherapy.
3. Self-help groups offer the mutual support of fellow stutterers striving together.

No other field has dealt as extensively with stuttering as has speech pathology. It is the profession that has been responsible for developing the major methods of therapy and prevention. It is also the field that has done vastly more research on stuttering than any other profession. Since you are most likely to seek the service of a speech clinician if you need professional help, I will discuss what you could expect from such service.

## Fluency-Management and Counseling Therapies

Fluency-management and counseling therapies can be used to great benefit. Most everyone who stutters wants to be free of having to struggle to speak. The idea of being able to speak fluently is tremendously appealing. Fluency management is frequently used with children as well as adults. The procedures described here are for those who have not successfully outgrown their stuttering.

My colleagues and I have used fluency procedures for over a quarter century. For improving fluency in children, gradual increases in the length of their statements is especially effective. It is also useful with teens and adults, but usually as a supplement to fluency skills. Air-flow skills are effective with many, but are not as guaranteed to produce fluency as are rate-control skills. Even though it takes a slow drone to be fluent without exception, most everyone is thrilled at first just to drone fluently. With more sophisticated skills than rate control, normal-sounding speech can be achieved quickly. But it does not feel normal. The fluency honeymoon lasts about three weeks. Then reality begins to set in. To use these skills requires constant attention to how to speak fluently rather than how to communicate. What people begin to realize is that their dream of controlled fluency eventually becoming automatic and normal, if they just work at it long enough, will never happen.

The idea of being free of stuttering is tremendously enticing. I was certainly enticed by it for years. My colleagues and I were thrilled and satisfied that we could work with virtually any persons who stuttered, regardless of severity or age, and within weeks they would sound like normally fluent speakers. Our objective was to keep them in this state of freedom from stuttering. What puzzled us was why they had trouble using controlled speech to remain fluent in tough speaking situations.

Our first clue that we were not solving all problems was when our people who stuttered insisted forcefully that what *sounded* like normal fluency certainly didn't *feel* normal. They were so busy concentrating on the me-

*What being patronized means to anyone, not just children who stutter, is that we think they cannot compete on equal footing, so they have to be extended special privileges.*

*Assertiveness-conflict stuttering is an explicit protest against being patronized, which is the ultimate insult.*

chanics of fluency that they couldn't attend to the idea they were trying to communicate. Moreover, not one of them felt cured. Regardless of how normal they sounded, they always felt that stuttering hovered in the background, waiting for the opportunity to leap out.

None of this made any sense to me until I finally realized that what I heard as stuttering was not necessarily real stuttering. It sounded abnormal to me, but it didn't feel like stuttering to the speaker. People know they have stuttered when their throats, mouths, and chests tighten and they lose control of their speech when they involuntarily trip or become stuck trying to talk. That is real stuttering. What the rest of us hear may sound like stuttering when it doesn't feel like stuttering. That is a false alarm.

Our concentration on maintaining fluency was like assuming that by hiding stuttering, it would eventually go away. Obviously, that is not the way to prevent it. To reduce real stuttering requires preventing or minimizing the causes of loss of control. When that is the focus of treatment, then reduction of what we hear as stuttering is a good sign that the problem of loss of control is improving, even though some of the stuttering may be a false alarm.

The alternative, and desired, goal is to use fluency management skills as a safety net in a program designed to build confidence. Confidence is achieved with success in speaking out openly and spontaneously, whether stuttering occurs or not. This is what Aileen was talking about. It cannot be achieved as long as the speaker harbors doubts. Those doubts are preserved by avoiding words, people, situations or anything else in which stuttering might occur. Fluency management and counseling, when used as a safety net to strengthen ability to run the risks of speaking out, provide a relatively rapid method of building confidence.

Another advantage is that fluency and counseling programs stress self-management. Stutterers are taught the tools with which they can manage their own speech destiny. These tools can be used to meet ever-expanding challenges. When the challenge is to prove to themselves that they are as free to speak as anyone else, then fluency management and counseling provide powerful tools for building confidence.

*Remember that fluency is not the objective of therapy. This point cannot be stressed too much.*

## Stuttering-Management and Counseling Therapies

Stuttering-management and counseling therapies are after much the same results as the best of fluency-management therapies: avoidance reduction. But they go about it differently. Although some fluency skills are used to help reduce severity of stuttering, the emphasis from the outset is on confronting fear of stuttering with no avoidances permitted. This means analyzing what is done during stuttering and going into speaking situations that would otherwise be avoided. The predictable consequence is a goodly amount of stuttering, but that is the objective: to stutter openly. This way the intent is that stutterers will discover that they need not fear and avoid it.

*You will be sorely tempted to think of maintaining fluency as the most important accomplishment. Nothing could be farther from the truth.*

To ease the trauma of this approach, the emphasis is on group support. A sort of "us against the world" quality develops from which individual members gain strength and confidence. Instead of the emphasis being on self-management, it is on group allegiance and loyalty in a common cause.

The stuttering management and counseling approach is reflected in some excellent suggestions designed to reduce a child's struggles with stuttering. The assumption underlying these suggestions is that what you hear as stuttering is the problem. Accordingly, the recommendations are intended primarily to lessen the difficulty with speaking when children stutter. They differ from the foregoing prevention strategies in that they are not designed to cope specifically with the different causes of stuttering, nor to reduce its addictiveness.

The Speech Foundation of America, a non-profit organization devoted exclusively to the welfare of people who stutter, has a series of publications. One, *Do You Stutter?: A Guide for Teens*, has excellent suggestions for how teens can cope with stuttering. Another, *Stuttering and Your Child: Questions and Answers*, has a rich supply of things to do and not to do. Here are some excerpts.

**Things parents can do to help the child who stutters:**

- Listen patiently to what your child says, not how it is said. Respond to the message rather than the stuttering.
- Allow your child to complete his thoughts without interrupting.

- Keep natural eye contact while your child is talking.

- Avoid filling in or speaking your child's thoughts or ideas. Let the words be his own.

- After your child speaks, reply slowly and unhurriedly, using some of the same words.  For example, if he says, "I s-s-see the b-b-b-bunny." You reply in an easy relaxed way, "oh yes, you see the bunny. He's cute."

- Wait a second or so before responding to your child. This helps to calm and slow things down and should help his speech.

- Make a point of commenting on what the child says, not the way he says it.

-  Ask fewer questions. When questions are asked, ask one at a time and give the child ample time to answer.

- Spend at least 5 minutes each day devoted to  talking with your child in an unhurried, easy, relaxed manner.

- Find ways to show your child that you love and value him and that you enjoy your time together.

*Once the image of stutterer has been established, with stuttering to protect it, prevention is no longer a possibility.*

**Things that HELP:**

- Provide a calmer, less-hurried life style in the home.
- Speak less hurriedly when talking to the child.
- Allow the child to finish his thoughts.
- Try not to talk for the child or rush him to finish his thoughts.
- Turn off the television and radio during dinner time; this is a time for family conversation not listening to television or radio programs.

*What can be accomplished, with professional help, is improvement to the extent that stuttering can be reduced to a manageable part of life.*

• If your child begins to talk to you while you are doing things that require concentration (for example, driving a car, using a knife to cut vegetables) tell him that you can't look away right now but that you are listening to him and that he has your attention.

**Things that HINDER:**

• Finishing the child's sentences.

• Rushing the child to finish his thought or sentences.

• Interrupting the child while he is talking.

• Encouraging or requiring him to talk rapidly, precisely and maturely at all times.

• Frequently correcting, criticizing, or trying to change the way he talks, or pronounces sounds or words.

• Speaking to the child using a rapid rate of speech, especially when telling him to slow his own rate of speaking down.

• Maintaining an overly rapid life-style within the home (or constantly feeling or acting as if "everything had to be done yesterday").

• Making him give little speeches, plays or read aloud to visiting friends, relatives or neighbors.

**What baby-sitters can do to help:**

• Treat the child who stutters like all the other children you baby-sit.

- Don't let him get away with things that his brothers and sisters aren't allowed to do.
- Here are a few "don'ts" that will help:
    (a) don't hurry the child's speech
    (b) don't finish words or sentences for him
    (c) don't interrupt
    (d) don't correct pronunciations
    (e) don't keep the child from talking
- Be patient and pay attention to what the child says, not how he says it. Respond to the message.

*When assertiveness-conflict stuttering appears during preschool years, the possibility of successful prevention falls squarely on parents.*

**What the day care center can do to help:**
- Treat the child who stutters the same as the other children at the center.
- Don't let the child who stutters get away with things just because he stutters.
- View the stuttering as making some mistakes in the normal learning process. This child should be encouraged to express ideas just as any other child at the center.
- When he has disruption in speech, allow him time to work through the mistakes:
    (a) without listeners hurrying him.
    (b) without listeners finishing words or ideas for him.
- The child who stutters should receive the same discipline as any other child.

*When chronic, the prospect of stuttering will still remain, but will be far enough out of sight and out of mind that it will not be a major problem.*

- The child who stutters should learn the same talking manners as any other child; for example, (a) taking turns talking, (b) listening while others talk, and (c) not interrupting others or finishing their words or ideas for them.

**What a teacher can do to help:**

- Meeting with parents of a child who stutters before or near the beginning of classes will help you learn the parents' concerns and expectations.
- If there is a speech clinician at your school, contact her to see what suggestions she may have for this child. If she is working with him, find out what her objectives are.
- Encourage good talking manners in the classroom: no one interrupts, talks for or finishes words for anyone else.
- Don't let the child who stutters get away with things just because he stutters.
- As much as possible, treat the child who stutters the same as the other children in your class—with the exception of special assistance with oral recitations.
- Children who stutter should be expected to perform all classroom oral recitation even though they may need some special help to succeed.
- Talk with the child about the oral recitation requirements, how he feels about it and what you can do to help.
- Give the child a chance to practice his oral recitation requirements at home, and encourage him.

- Allow children who stutter enough time to talk; they may frequently have trouble starting to talk.
- Know that your caring enough to do these things can make a big difference.

*Equally important, the image of being a stutterer can be all but eliminated.*

## Self-Help Groups

Self-help groups achieve much the same allegiance and support as is provided by stuttering-management programs. Rather than going forth to face up to stuttering in the outside world, the opportunity is provided within the group. These groups are growing in popularity. They are comprised mainly of adults, and occasionally teens, most of whom expect to stutter for the rest of their lives.

## Psychotherapy

Psychotherapy is predictably effective in improving how people who stutter feel about themselves. Few clinical psychologists or psychiatrists have much experience with stuttering, however, so the therapy they provide is more likely to address general problems of adjustment than the specific causes of stuttering. Having had experience with all of these approaches, I think that psychotherapy would be optimally effective if it were provided in conjunction with a confidence-building fluency- or stuttering-management program. The actual successes

*Fluency management and counseling, when used as a safety net to strengthen ability to run the risks of speaking out, provide a relatively rapid method of building confidence.*

essential to building confidence would come from the speaking requirements in these programs.

These types of therapy are different enough that one would expect them to yield different results. To the contrary, such evidence as is available suggests that the results of fluency-management, stuttering-management, and self-help approaches are remarkably the same. The common thread running through these approaches is confidence. When people who stutter are confident, they seem to feel free to speak out with the expectation of being successful communicators. With increased confidence goes increased security and decreased stuttering. Because psychotherapy can also improve confidence, the likelihood is that it, too, if used in conjunction with a program fostering success in speaking out in increasingly difficult situations, would be equally successful.

## Finding Professional Help

If you need professional help, the most appropriate profession for you to consider is speech pathology. I have not included psychiatry because, as yet, there is no effective medical treatment, even on the horizon. For help with anything directly concerned with stuttering, including management of speech rate in the family, speech clinicians who have specialized in treatment of stuttering in children are apt to have the most experience. Moreover, many speech clinicians have experience with counseling and psychotherapy for speech problems.

How to decide which one to choose requires more detailed information. Speech clinicians should be certified and licensed. The American Speech-Language-Hearing Association certifies clinical competence in therapy of speech and language disorders. The state in which a clinician practices provides licensing. In those states which license these professions, it is illegal to be in private practice without it. The standards for licensing in speech pathology are roughly the same as for certification by the profession.

Having established these basic qualifications, equally important selections still remain. Within any profession are specializations. Not all speech clinicians have much experience with stuttering, nor do they all have extensive experience with children's language. Clinicians who specialize in both of these areas are relatively rare. The Speech Foundation of America (P.O. Box 11749, Memphis, TN 38111 / 1-800-992-9392) is devoted entirely to the welfare of people who stutter. It is the best source I know for information on clinicians in your location who have experience with children who stutter.

The best way to find the help you seek is by recommendation of someone whose judgment you trust who understands the help you need. Short of that, the next best alternative, once you have found potential clinicians, is to meet with them, form your own impressions of the models they would be for your child, and whether they would be able to help you achieve your objective.

The recommendations I have made for prevention are based on new information. This means that you will need to describe in some detail what you hope to accomplish.

*The stuttering management and counseling approach is reflected in some excellent suggestions designed to reduce a child's struggles with stuttering.*

*When people who stutter are confident, they seem to feel free to speak out with the expectation of being successful communicators.*

Finally, they may be willing to put you in touch with several families they have helped. Therapy is an inexact art. Failures are inevitable. Willingness of clinicians to tell you about their failures tells you much about their credibility. You will need someone whose competence goes beyond technique, someone who radiates caring, and someone who is as straightforward, honest, and open as you will be trying to be with your child.

# Section VI: Appendix

*With increased confidence goes increased security and decreased stuttering.*

The following article by Dr. Richard Mallard, of South-west Texas State University, is reprinted from *Seminars in Speech and Language*. It is an account of David, almost five, who had been stuttering for over two years when this report of "Talk Time" began. The first eight sessions describe what went on between David and his parents. This activity is particularly useful with preschool children. How each reacted is revealing of what you could expect if you decide to use any of the procedures in Strategy 6.

The activity from "Third Therapy Session" on could be used with a child of any age. From the description, you can decide for yourself whether to attempt this without a therapist. Obviously, chances of success are better if one is available.

*Who you would need for a clinician is someone whose competence goes beyond technique, someone who radiates caring, and someone who is as straight-forward, honest, and open as you will be trying to be with your child.*

# Family Intervention In Stuttering Therapy

## A. R. Mallard, Ph.D.

Reprinted from: *Seminars in Speech and Language*

Six years ago we at Southwest Texas State University began a family-oriented stuttering program for children (Mallard, 1985) patterned after the program by Rustin (1987). Our goal was to involve the entire family in therapy in order to increase carryover. As of this writing, we have seen 22 families, and 18 of the stuttering children (82%) have not been enrolled in speech therapy following our program. These results indicate that our success with stuttering children increased when we involved the family in therapy from the outset.

The stuttering child, a male named David, was four years, nine months old at the time of the interview. There was one other child in the home, a sister, Nancy, who was 19 months. The father described David as an active boy with a strong personality "who tests the limits of parental authority quite frequently." The father described himself as extroverted, gregarious, high achieving, and a people person. He also described himself as one "who often concentrates on something and tunes everything else out. This can sometimes be frustrating to my family when they're trying to get my attention." He apparently stuttered as a small child, according to reports from his mother. No evidence of dysfluency in his speech was noted. The mother described David as being close to her. "At times he can be rather rejecting of his father. At other times he is very interested in being just like his daddy."

The mother indicated that David felt frustrated and competitive with his sister at times, especially for his mother's attention. The mother valued her relationship with her mother and father "very much." She described herself as a nurturing, devoted mother—sometimes overprotective. She also indicated she was "perfectionistic, intense, takes things seriously, and introverted."

The parents described the onset of David's stuttering at 21 months, when Nancy was two weeks of age. The mother said, "I panicked" at the onset. "I felt awful about it. I felt like it was my fault." When asked if the problem bothered her, the response was, "Oh yes, it does me." The father did not notice the problem as soon as the mother. He indicated that he was not alarmed by the dysfluency. "It has affected me in our family in my trying to deal with my wife about it." David's speech was reportedly characterized by repetition of the first sounds of words. The parents indicated that the speech pattern had changed in the last few months with the addition of sound prolongations and elevation of fundamental frequency. The father described the problem as not being "too severe" and the mother rated the problem "moderate." Both agreed that David seemed to stutter more with the mother than the father.

Both parents came from significantly different backgrounds. The mother's father had a drinking problem, the family moved frequently, and her parents were divorced when she was 13. She described her family as "complicated." The father, on the other hand, described his family as "stable." The father was the sole source of income for the family. His job took him away from the home during many evenings and weekends. Consequently, the children were with the mother most of the time.

At the time of the interview, David was dysfluent on approximately 19% of words spoken during conversational speech. The dysfluencies included inappropriate breathing patterns, elevation of fundamental frequency, and sound, syllable, and word repetition. Struggle behaviors included laryngeal tension exhibited as glottal fry and cessation of the speech attempt. Expressive and receptive language, bilateral hearing, and articulation were within normal limits.

It is a standard procedure, following the interview, that the family is given an assignment called "Talk Time." The entire family is brought into the therapy room. We explain that we are going to give some "homework" to the parents. The following instructions are read verbatim:

> This activity is called "Talk Time." It has nothing to do with stuttering. It is a task for the parents, not the child. Listen to

the instructions to determine if you would like to participate. "Talk Time" should be conducted for 3, 4, or 5 minutes several times a week. Your child should find any toy that he/she likes. After the toy is chosen, go into his/her room and close the door. Set a clock for the time that you choose. During that time your job is to talk with him/her. Do not bombard the child with questions—just talk. During this time, your speech rate should be a little bit slower. Lay back and enjoy this time together. You are to devote all your energies to listening to your child. Don't think about your work, cooking, etc., just listen to what is said, not how it is said. This assignment must not be completed while watching television or reading. Also, it must not be done in the automobile. It must be in the child's room where you can be on the same eye level with him/her. Sit or lie on the floor together or where there is not a height difference between the two of you. At the end of the specified time, you are to praise him/her. Say, "Thank you" and leave. Do not go beyond the specified time period. That will defeat the purpose of the assignment. Immediately upon completion of the task, fill in the task sheet. At the end of each week, mail the task sheet to me. I shall respond immediately with comments or suggestions.

The child is asked if he/she will agree to help the parents. If the child agrees, the minutes (3, 4, or 5) and the number of times during the week (usually no more than two or three per parent) are negotiated. The times are confirmed with the child as the negotiation proceeds from minutes to days. The parents are reminded to select times that will be easy to accomplish. David agreed to have a talk time with mother three times a week for five minutes and with father two times a week for five minutes.

A task sheet is to be returned each week on which each parent describes the activity and indicates how they feel about the time spent with their child. The written instructions are given to the parents to take home. A brief note (two or three paragraphs) is written to the family as each task sheet is returned. The note contains comments about the homework and suggestions if needed.

The following are direct quotes from the task sheets. Notice that the observations made by the parents about their behavior set the stage for eventual intervention. This article was submitted to the parents for their review. They were asked to make reflective comments about issues that were the most significant for them. The mother provided valuable insights concerning issues that had to be resolved and personal feelings that surfaced throughout the therapy process. Both parent's post-therapy reflections are so indicated. You will notice that therapy for the child required effort, change, and adjustment for the parents. This is why we believe the parents must be the focus of therapy for the stuttering child.

*Talk Time One:* Mother: When I'm trying to remember not to ask questions, I don't listen to David well. I want to feel more relaxed as we do this. It was neat to see David so excited about our special time. I enjoyed our conversation and his enthusiasm. I like this time that's just ours, with no agenda or pressure. It's hard for me not to focus on his dysfluency when he's talking.

Father: I found it pretty difficult not to ask him a lot of questions. I felt good about his interest, although I felt that most of the time we didn't talk much. I noticed that he was having some dysfluency.

*Talk Time Two:* Mother: Nice time—I felt less pressure to make it go well. I think David is anxious to have talk time with Daddy. It is hard for me not to be in my "parent" role, i.e., explaining all the time, and just listen and let him carry the ball. Interesting difference from yesterday when I thought I talked all the time. It was great being caught up in David's fantasy. Really relaxing and enjoyable. David and I need more one on one time, I think.

Father: I found it a little easier not to ask so many questions. David is very fluent. I felt kind of bad about the way our time was dominated by these discipline concerns. It was kind of a disaster since we were in our room, he was distracted by all the "forbidden fruit."

*Talk Time Three:* Mother: It was great. I think for the 1st time fluency or disfluency didn't cross my mind. We were just together, talking, having fun. I felt frustrated with me. I was thinking, "Just shut up!" If he's not talkative, I just start to fill up the time so we'll be talking. Except I'm talking. I was more conscious of listening but it didn't seem awkward. David has been quite fluent. It was a fun and amusing discussion. I paid more attention to listening and David was very persuasive.

Father: It was really hard again not to ask questions. David always asks a lot of questions about when it will be over. We had a little trouble because I had just disciplined him and that bled over a little into talk time. I tried to let him initiate most of the conversation so I wouldn't lapse into asking too many questions.

*Talk Time Four:* Mother: I felt rather at a loss when he happily suggested activities where I would be doing all the talking. I don't think he wanted to avoid talking, but he enjoys being read to and playing "This Little Piggy." I felt the time had a negative overtone. I was very irritated because he seemed determined to test limits. I corrected him the whole time. I was relieved we did better. I was more aware of looking straight at David when I'm listening. David was very amusing and talkative. I love observing his creative and thoughtful mind. Basically, I said very little.

Father: I felt pretty good about this talk time. I didn't ask many questions and he talked freely. I felt good about it. Both of us were relaxed. Little or no dysfluency. I felt good about the time. I didn't ask too many questions.

*Talk Time Five:* Mother: Very relaxing and positive time. It seemed easy. Truthfully, I was sick of being around him since he was acting so whiny. I was kind of doing it out of obligation. I felt bad about being so impatient and tried to act more friendly and engaging. I think he was rather sick of me, too. I was (and still am) mad at him and myself for waiting so late in the day. He was uncooperative and I was impatient.

Father: It went well, although sometimes he was quiet and I felt like we should talk all the time. I felt very good about it. I have been pleased because he seemed to be identifying with me more. Lately we have been through a difficult period in our relationship. I felt good about the time. We were both relaxed and enjoyed it.

*Talk Time Six:* Mother: David was mildly interested and then very easily distracted. He kept wanting to leave to get something else. I felt frustrated over his inattention but I didn't want to spend the whole time correcting him. David was happy to have talk time and was interested in discussing getting married. He was mildly distractible, but was more cooperative in interacting. I was relieved things went more smoothly. David was quite cooperative and more talkative than he has been lately. He was mildly dysfluent and talked louder during these times. I enjoyed this talk time and being with David. I feel bad and helpless when he's dysfluent.

David was very wound up and talked almost non-stop about several subjects. He wasn't dysfluent at all that I noticed but he was talking very rapidly. Usually he's more likely to be dysfluent at those times. I felt good and enjoyed our talk time. David didn't seem as distracted, and I felt we really focused on each other.

Father: We talked about his dolls and about boys and girls. It went real smoothly. I felt real good about it. Little or no dysfluency, also. We talked about navy ships and airplanes. David likes talking about that—took up the whole time. It went real well.

The family met with me at my office following this assignment. The father was noticing less dysfluency.

David was not repeating syllables and words and there was no elevation of fundamental frequency. Stuttering was reportedly not present during talk time. David seemed to be worse when talking out of turn. He refused to be quiet when asked. The mother noticed more dysfluency when David was trying to tell something, trying to get attention, or when a lot of people were around and he was competing for talking time. Speech was noted to be worse during arguments. Observing herself, the mother noted, " . . . how parenting I am all the time." She commented on how important the social setting was with regard to David's stuttering.

> *Mother's Reflection:* . . . I was saying the social setting was important to me because I felt so self-conscious when David was dysfluent around other people. That was a major issue that I had to deal with in therapy—being worried of what others thought about David and me when he stuttered. Naturally, I expected them to blame me.
>
> Another thing that I was wondering at that time was if David was more dysfluent when we were away from home because I was on his case all the time—"Leave that alone, don't touch this, get away from there."

The talk time assignment was changed. Each parent was to have one talk time per week and mail the sheet every other week. They were to write their turn taking and interruption patterns at home on the back of the sheet.

> *Talk Time Seven:* Mother: It was hilarious to listen to his tunes and lyrics, especially, "Love Your Mamma." I wish I had

it on tape. Nice time with no dysfluency that I noticed. David wasn't as disappointed when we ended, much to my relief.

Father: He was pretty animated and had no stuttering. It was an enjoyable time. It went very well. He seemed to enjoy it a lot also and talked quite freely.

*Comments about Turn Taking*: Mother: Our turntaking issue is a struggle, although I think David realized I mean it and will punish him if he doesn't cooperate. He pushes me more when others are present—maybe he thinks I won't force the issue with others around. Anyway, we're all learning. I'm telling myself I have the right not to listen to him all the time. David is learning he doesn't always come first, no matter how frantic he gets.

Father: We are finding that firmness regarding this is effective. I am making an effort to be more firm regarding other disciplinary measures. It is a constant battle, though. I think discipline is about the most significant issue we've hit upon. (Note: This is an important statement that will be addressed later in therapy.).

*Mother's Reflection*: I just could not/would not accept that discipline was a factor for so long. I'm not sure why. Maybe because I didn't think he was dysfluent on purpose (which I still don't) or that he would even unconsciously use it to get attention. I felt so sorry for him and so guilty that I was blind to this obvious truth. It was as if I could love him out of the stuttering, just give him more and more. Children don't need everything we have—they need the things that best prepare them for real life.

*Talk Time Eight*: Mother: It was nice being together. I had to force myself not to get uptight when he stuttered. I was pretty irritated and felt impatient when he became dysfluent. I feel bad that so much of my communication with him is correction or no-nos.

Father: David was very excited to talk—was animated—no stuttering. An enjoyable time. David was very gregarious and he seemed to enjoy the time very much.

*Comments about Turn Taking*: Mother: We are still plugging away with taking turns. Some progress, I think. Also, a new area for me to consider is just establishing a quiet time for David, or he'll talk constantly. I waiver between being wishy-washy (what decent mother doesn't always listen to her little darling?) or wanting to scream, "Will you shut up?"

*Mother's Reflection*: I am still struggling with the issue of when I come first, what I have the right to expect and receive, and that I can still be a good mother and not live and breathe 24 hours a day for my children.

The father made no comments about turn taking this week.

I called the mother following this assignment. She stated that "David gets on my nerves." Her feelings about the stuttering changed from fear to irritation. She didn't know what to do. She feared that her time with David and her husband's time were very different. The husband was so laid back and she was so uptight. We decided to begin therapy on a weekly basis the following month.

*First Therapy Session*: The focus of this session was to introduce the program we would follow. We discussed several theories about the onset and development of stuttering, discussed the role of the parents in therapy, and reviewed factors that affect fluency. The importance of parents knowing what to observe as speech changes was emphasized. An observation handout was discussed. Their homework assignment for the week was to observe David during the week and write their observations on the task sheet.

*Second Therapy Session*: Each therapy session always starts with a discussion of the homework from the previous meeting.

*Comments on Homework*: Mother: David had talked to his grandmother on the telephone and demonstrated controlled speech. I was very surprised and happy because David can be hard to understand, especially on the phone. He remained calm enough to talk—my mom was impressed, too. I wasn't surprised but didn't get too uptight. This situation—group with lots of stimulation—seems to be a common problem for him. It's hard for me to walk the fine line between listening appropriately and tolerating endless arguing. He's more dysfluent. I feel TRAPPED!

Father: I feel good about the fact that his stuttering on the first sound of words has improved. I feel badly because I haven't had much time to observe David these last few days.

The mother's comment about David's performance on the telephone was "excited, surprised, impressed and relieved." The mother described a situation in which David was talking with the baby-sitter, speaking fast and stuttering. I asked the mother what she did. She said, "I wanted to say, 'David can you please slow down?' But I didn't. I just observed. This was hard."

> *Mother's Reflection*: I remember during therapy being frustrated that there wasn't some clear and concise way to fix it— to help him, make him stop stuttering. And, I wanted you to tell me what it was and how to do it. Sometimes I just wanted to shake you and say, "Take care of it now!"

She also indicated that the previous day had been difficult. David was not minding. She indicated,

> There is a conflict. I want to listen to my child. I want some back and forth interaction. I don't want to have to experience this back and forth bickering every time I tell him to do something. I feel trapped.

She indicated that her feelings of being trapped made her feel like a failure as a mother. "I have such high expectations of being a mother." The father indicated that his wife wonders, "What have I done to cause this stuttering."

> *Mother's Reflection*: One reason I felt I had done something was the so-called child experts (our family doctor and David's Mother's Day Out teacher), I asked about David's stuttering before we consulted you, told me it was caused by stress in the home. I was home with him the most and either I was contributing to it or I wasn't shielding him from it, or so I thought.

It appeared from this conversation that discipline was going to be a key factor in therapy. David apparently created havoc with the mother and she did not know what to do. The mother again indicated that she felt trapped by David's talking and arguing.

A brief conversation was conducted concerning why David stuttered more with mother than with dad. Again, mother felt like David's stuttering was her fault or that the stuttering was related to her. The mother indicated it was terribly hard just to observe and not tell David what to do. She did not feel she was objective with her observation. She felt pain when he was dysfluent and she did not believe her husband felt the same way. The mother indicated she was an absolute "basket case" when David started stuttering. The father did not believe he felt the same way: he could observe without telling David what to do.

While listing on the board what you learn from observing, the father said, "So many times a person responds by what he sees. The person with a problem gets a lot of cues from the environment on how to react." The mother then indicated that she really feels for David when he stutters and believed that stuttering gets him all kinds of attention! This was especially relevant to the timing of the stuttering onset coincident with the birth of the sister, and could have explained how David was using disfluency to get his way.

The assignment for the following week was to be aware of what David was observing in them. Also, the parents were asked to note who talks, interrupts, and listens the most in the family.

*Third Therapy Session*: The parents agreed that David interrupts most in the family. The father tends not to listen sometimes, and the mother talks the most. David also talks frequently and tends to interrupt. The father related that he believed it was hard for David to get his attention. He may be giving signals that he, the father, is too busy to listen. David keeps talking when the dad is not listening. David must do something "real bad" for him to listen!  David asked his father one day, "Why do you yell at me all the time?"  A discussion then occurred about David's manipulative behavior. The mother indicated that she did not know what to do when he was trying to ma-nipulate her. She should not have to feel guilty when she does not give in. The mother was asked how she felt about herself. She stated, as she started to cry,

> I'm learning to like myself. It's hard to put limits on David. It's connected, I think, to my background. I am the youngest of four girls. I was Dad's pet. I was always the peacemaker in the family. My father was an alcoholic and it was my job to keep Daddy acting nice to everyone. My mother had to support the family and did not have time for me emotionally. I now feel that I have to protect David the same way I did with my family. Liking myself and accepting myself are hard for me where the kids are concerned. I don't want them to feel abandoned. When our little unplanned Nancy came along I didn't think it would be good for David. I'm just bitchy, not as good natured as I could be. I don't know what a normal home like is like.

She further stated that the "peacemaker" role, "always walking on eggshells," caused her to feel guilty having to make normal responses to the children when it came to discipline. "I am doing the same thing as a big girl that I did as a little girl and David knows how to get to me."

The homework comments of the mother were especially relevant:

> I hated this exercise. All along I've thought I was a good mother, concerned about my children and sensitive to their needs. And I saw many examples of how I listen or don't listen when David talks. A lot of times I'm rushing him, just get it over with. Or, I'm telling him to talk softer, or I'm listening second hand while I cook, clean, or read. Or I walk out of the room, maintaining that I'm still paying attention. I feel awful, like a real insensitive clod. Just what I need.

> *Mother's Reflection*: It was and is very hard for me to put into words what I wanted to say then, to explain my feelings and how they relate to David. My family was so dysfunctional and preoccupied with my Dad's drinking binges and my older sister's escapades that I felt very overshadowed. Even in the most basic things my parents (my mother especially) did not have the time or emotional energy to deal with me. I felt very abandoned and alone, but I also learned to just try real hard to handle things myself. I'm dependent in some ways but very independent in others. Maybe controlling would describe it better! I want to take care of things myself—my way. It's more predictable for me and I know what to expect. It wasn't easy for me to come to you for that reason. Anyway, since I felt that my parents didn't help me much in my everyday struggles with growing up I was determined that my children would not feel

that way or experience that. And when I worried about David being ridiculed in social setting or school and feeling the pain of that, I felt in advance that pain for him, too. I wanted to spare him that and was willing to endure it for him as much as I could. I would rather feel it than him. I remember so clearly you saying to me, "You can't shield him from all the pains of life." I didn't say what I was thinking because I knew it was irrational, but I could feel myself tensing up on the inside with this steely determination, and almost with clenched fists I thought, "You want to bet? Just watch me." Realizing that that was not only impossible but not good for David in the long run was very difficult. Knowing that I could be a good mother and still set limits on what my children demanded from me and what I wanted for myself meant that I had to let go of some of the garbage that tied me to my past. As I did a little bit at a time and it felt good, it encouraged me to do it more. Seeing David handling things pretty well on his own showed me he really wasn't so fragile after all. And, wanting him to be prepared for life and all its ups and downs more than I wanted a perpetual baby forced me to rethink some things.

The father indicated that he realized it is hard to get his attention and that most of his interaction with David was correction:

This was pretty difficult. I feel like at times the cues I send to David are that I am more inaccessible to him, that I have more important things to do than play, talk, or listen unless he is misbehaving. That's a sure way to get my attention.

It was obvious from this session that the mother needed a strategy for disciplining the children that would not add to her feelings of inadequacy. The decision was made to begin problem solving next week even though this was a topic that was normally discussed at a later time in therapy. The parents were asked to bring David for the next meeting. This would be his first session. A specific homework assignment was not made.

*Fourth Therapy Session*: Since problem solving is such a critical topic in this course, the instructions are presented below. The goal of this therapy is to get the family to see stuttering as a problem that can have many possible solutions. We want the child to understand that the key to solving the stuttering problem is to identify what options he/she wants to put into effect and then help the parents let the child experience the resulting consequences. The following instructions are read verbatim:

Problem solving is one of the most important skills that you will learn in this course. This technique can be used to solve all types of problems, not just stuttering. The steps are as follows: First, identify the problem. This can be very difficult. You must, however, be specific about what the exact problem is. Write the problem in the middle of the paper and draw a circle around it. Second, list all possible options around the circle, no matter how far out or silly. Third, erase the ones that are really not options for your family. Fourth, list the options in order of their likelihood of happening for you. Fifth, discuss the consequences of the options you listed. Sixth, put into practice the option that you wish. Seventh, be satisfied with your decision. Be happy that you are calling your own shots. If other people don't like what you have decided, then it is their problem, not yours. Eighth, reevaluate this process and your decision after a short period of time.

The first problem that is solved has nothing to do with speech. The problem that was identified for this activity was the children touching the controls on the VCR when they were not supposed to. This was a significant session in that we saw for the first time how the family interacted. This experience was enough to convince all concerned that it is a must to work with the entire family if one expects to involve the parents in a significant manner!

As we went through the problem solve, David was uncontrollable. He would not sit still. He was up and down, twisting and turning in his seat. He wanted to switch chairs with his mother. She complied. The father interrupted David's suggestions three times. David would try to get the mother's attention by putting his face close to hers, patting her face, interrupting, touching her, etc. She would not tell him to quit and became increasingly upset with his behavior. The father made no attempts to assist. David would turn to his father for support when his mother would try to control him. It became apparent that discipline was a major factor in this family and that the parents were not working together. It appeared the parents left the session feeling somewhat embarrassed about David's behavior although nothing was said directly.

*Mother's Reflection:* I cringed reading this section. Not only was I embarrassed by David's behavior but my own, and I left that day absolutely furious with myself for letting him manipulate me and get away with murder. It was after this session that I had to admit, as much as I hated to, that disciplining David was a real problem for our whole family and obviously played at least some part in the speech situation.

*Fifth Therapy Session:* This session was totally different from a behavioral control standpoint. The parents were attempting to control David's behavior from the outset. The father took a much more active role and supported the mother's attempts. At one point, the father spanked David for not minding.

The purpose of this session was to videotape a problem–solve that the parents conducted. The tape would be taken home and studied for the week's assignment. A transcript was made of this session. The mother had 65 interactions in the session, 14 were corrections of David (22%), 2 were praises (3%). The father had 49 interactions, 15 were corrections (31%), and 1 praise (2%). All total, there were 114 parental interactions during the session, 29 were corrections (25%), and 3 were praises (3%). David made 49 statements during the session and 11 of those (22%) were interruptions when one of the parents was talking. It should be mentioned, however, that although this was not a normal conversational setting, the father reported in the case history and subsequent information that he did correct David frequently. Also, recall that both parents agreed that David did interrupt during normal conversations. Being able to observe this on tape proved to be significant for the parents.

The notes that were made during this session included better behavior control by the parents. It did appear, however, that the parents expected too much for a five-year old to sit still for one hour and may have overreacted to David's behavior. The parents negotiated possible solutions well. Family problems tended to relate to the children's behavior. The mother would make a suggestion and look to David for approval.

> *Mother's Reflection*: I also left that session feeling that my husband and I were too quick to jump on David during this session. We were probably overcompensating for being so wishy-washy the week before. And, it's hard to behave normally when you know you're being observed and videotaped. One more observation about the videotape. When my husband and I took it home and watched it, we felt very differently about it. He thought it proved his point of our need to control David more effectively. I thought it showed clearly how rigid and demanding I thought my husband was at times with David. We were absolutely furious with each other—I can hardly remember a time when I have been so angry with him, and at that time our relationship dated back 13 years earlier! We stopped the tape several times, rewound it, replayed it with, "Aha! See, I told you. There you are doing it again!" It was after this episode that it began to dawn on me just how much differently my husband and I saw this issue, and that he and I had a very significant situation between us to contend with. Still, we were both convinced we were right. When we came

to therapy and I saw that you tended to agree with his assessment it surprised me. I wanted to tell myself that it was because you are both fathers—perhaps authoritarian fathers at times. And, since my dad was in the Army, I grew up with more Army sergeant interaction and authoritarianism than I could hardly stand. I have almost an aversion to that—"Because I say so, that's why." But, since not only were you a father, you were also the supposed expert in this matter, I decided I had better give the possibility a little more consideration.

From this description you see how important it is to work with both parents. It is not uncommon for the mother and father to have differing views about issues that are discussed. It would obviously not be a good situation to have one parent returning from therapy and correcting the spouse!

The most significant statements during this session occurred when the father said they had tried problem solving before but, " . . . not in this much detail. We have done similar things but did not get input from the children."

The mother was relating that the solution the family reached during the week had worked well. The children had not tested the limits. "David realized we mean business since the family had decided on this." The father made the following statement:

> Another thing we had talked about before was lying. At first he did not admit it and then told the truth. He knows there are consequences now. I asked what he thought would be appropriate punishment. He suggested I spank him and I did. He responds better with limits and if we follow through.

It was important to note during the session that even though David's behavior was better, the parents had to spend a lot of time correcting him and he was still dominating the session with misbehavior.

*Sixth Therapy Session*: This turned out to be a significant session. The following illustrates the importance of problem solving and how solving problems in general can be related to how the family will eventually solve the problem of stuttering.

The mother reported that they really worked hard on this tape by watching it and making notes. They devised a "Basic Theory" for their family: "The parents do not interact with the children much unless the father is correcting the child's behavior." The father had to discipline David during the session by a light spanking and it upset the mother to watch. She indicated that her feelings probably go back to her family upbringing.

The parents noted that David was most upset when he did not get his way. When decisions were not made in his favor, he would become hard to manage. The parents said,

> The key issue with us in managing him is that it is okay to express opinions, but sometimes the parents have to make the final decision. When he rebels there will be negative consequences.

A discussion then followed concerning what type of decisions a five year old can make? Such things were discussed as what to wear or what to eat. This led to a discussion about David's making a decision as to whether or not he will work on his speech when he learns some speech control skills. Will they be able to accept his decision if the decision did not agree with what the parents thought should happen? Suppose David does not want to improve his speech? After all, it did appear, according to the mother, that stuttering was being reinforced by the mother's reactions. Can a child at five years determine how he talks? More importantly, can the parents of a five-year old allow the child to experience the consequences of his decisions?

The mother indicated that her concern was that other children will make fun of David. The following question was asked, "If he has skills to help him with his speech, are you willing to let him choose not to use them, even though others make fun?" The mother indicated, "Yes I'd let him because the consequences of forcing him are bad." This was a major breakthrough for the mother!

The discussion then centered on David's accepting consequences of his decisions. The mother indicated that she spends a lot of time anticipating his needs to keep him from having trouble. The discussion then centered on David using stuttering as a tool to get attention. According to the mother, his stuttering apparently gets him what he wants. The questions was, "Could David use stuttering as a tool or an asset?" The mother stated, "Yes he could." The father said, "Yes. I don't think he has but he definitely could because he uses every other tool!"

*Mother's Reflection*: The thought of David experiencing consequences was, truthfully, gut-wrenching. It still is. David is in school now, and although his speech is not dysfluent now like it was then, he still is out in the cold, cruel world (as cold and cruel as first grade can be!). But, I've had to let my baby go and I can't always be there with him. We have dealt with some more difficult situations since we've been here—being the new kid on the block and feeling left out or picked on. I have definitely suffered the most in these instances! David has been mildly disturbed by them, but he seems remarkably resilient (or thick-skinned, whichever the case may be). Again I have to ask myself if I'm not projecting my painful memories (being in the Army, we moved a lot), and if I'm not making mountains out of molehills. Or at least not giving David the credit to hang in there and go on.

At the close of this session, the mother, commenting about their progress thus far, made the following comment, "I am glad that we came for my own peace of mind. I have gained parenting skills that will help me with many areas."

*Mother's Reflection*: My comment about being glad we came for therapy because of other parenting/coping skills that I gained, regardless of speech concerns, cannot be stressed enough.

The homework was to let David experience consequences of his decisions. The mother chose not to intervene at least three times with his decisions this week and the father chose two times. They were to document the decisions on the task sheet, describing the situation and how they felt.

*Seventh Session*: It is at this point that the mother began to show real progress and insight.

Mother's report: Situation 1: The children were wrestling. I told them I was afraid they were being too rough. In a minute David's mouth and Nancy's head connected. The result was a busted lip and a lot of crying. I felt kind of sorry it happened but it wasn't a critical injury. Maybe he'll think twice next time.

Situation 2: It was cold outside and I gave David his coat. He preferred a light windbreaker so he wore his choice. Turns out the windbreaker was adequate. I liked this. I felt off the hook. I felt relieved—relief. Could it be I'm not always right? I felt fine.

Situation 3: David got up from his nap and we had a doctor's appointment. He insisted he didn't have to go to the bathroom before we left. I expected an emergency stop on the side of the road. Not only did we make it to the doctor, but he didn't go for a couple more hours. I thought it was amazing that I decided I knew his needs more than he did. It's a relief not to be responsible for everything. It makes me feel free.

The following comments were made to the mother:

This was excellent. Consider programming yourself to let him make these kinds of decisions and let him deal with the consequences. If you always assume the responsibility, then his problem is your problem. Begin to start thinking like you did with this exercise. When he makes his decision let him experience the consequences. The more you can do this the more chances he has to take responsibility to get his speech together.

The mother responded,

In order for David to get his speech together, he has to experience consequences. Maybe he'll realize the consequences are uncomfortable, so maybe he won't choose that again.

The response to the mother was,

There is no way that coming to speech therapy will do anything without him voluntarily taking control. There are no pills to cure stuttering. You need to let him choose to use these or not—it's his decision. He may have to hurt some. If he sees that his problem is your problem, there's no reason for him to give up stuttering. It's not the techniques you learn that are important: it is your ability to foster independent decision making that is the key to the child's eventual success.

The conversation then turned to children's decision making and how that might reflect on the parents. The clinician asked, "Does his stuttering reflect on you?" The mother reported that her mother has asked in the past what all goes on in their home that could affect David's speech. The mother was asked how independent she was from her family. The mother reported, "Very dependent." The suggestion was for the mother to become more independent. The mother then responded that she had always had to be a "good little girl" and her mother apparently thinks she (David's mother) is not perfect "but she wants me to be." It was obvious that the mother's family played a significant role in David's mother's life.

*Mother's Reflection*: My mother was very noncommittal at first about us coming to see you. And, after we started, she was very interested in everything, homework assignments, etc. She and I talked at length after each session about what we covered, what your options were about why people stutter. I had shared with her my fears that I had caused it, that I was foster-ing it. I then talked about your explanations regarding that, and all of the exercises we did. I thought she under-stood—that she heard me. But one day, when we were at my house, she made this off-the-cuff comment. We had been in therapy for some time and I thought we were making progress. Then, out of the blue, she said, "You know, I've watched you, and I don't see you doing anything different than other people do with their children, even though yours stutter." I honestly think she thought she was affirming me, complimenting me. But all I could think of was that she had been watching us, evaluating us, and all that time she really had blamed me. I was glad she was changing, perhaps, but that hurt a lot.

The following question was asked:

What if David doesn't choose to control his speech? Will you get and/or react to support from your husband or your mother? As long as you operate to please others you will never be satisfied. You don't have to report to your mother. Explain to her that you will tell her what you want her to know about

David's speech and that she is not to ask. The father reported that he did not know this was going on with his wife's mother.

Father: I would have told her to buzz off. My father has allowed me to be independent and my mother finally quit asking if I was prepared for certain situations. When I went to college I was very surprised to discover that I could make a 4.0 even without my mother there to nag me. When my mother tries to interfere, or make "suggestions," I tell her it's not her concern.

Father's report: Situation 1: David didn't want to get dressed and I was trying to convince him. I told him he couldn't go outside if he wasn't dressed. I told him he could remain undressed if he chose to. He did for a while and then he came and asked me to help him get dressed. This worked pretty well. When he chose to, he asked me to help him.

Situation 2: David wanted to wear his flip-flops to bed. At first I told him no, but decided to let him if he wanted to. I felt ridiculous.

The assignment for the next session was to do the consequences homework again. The father, before saying no the first time, was to count to five and let David make the decision. He was to praise David's ability to make a decision. The mother's homework remained the same as last week.

*Eighth Session*: The homework assignment was most significant. Several instances were described in which the mother had allowed the children to make their decisions and experience the consequences. Each instance will not be explained but the mother's note at the end of the homework sheet was as follows:

> I just want to say I love this exercise. It is such a relief to avoid all the screaming hassles. Just let him live with his choices and learn. Besides, it seems that David almost feels compelled to choose non-conformist behavior. It only adds fuel to his fire to insist with him that he do things my way. He refuses when he feels crowded in a corner. He's happy—or happier, and I am much happier. There are fewer arguments. It's teaching me a different frame of mind, a different way of looking at and evaluating things.

The reply was,

> This all applies to stuttering. You're doing exactly what we want. He's calling his own shots and living with the consequences.

The mother responded,

> I can't make him stop stuttering. I guess I can only step back.

The remainder of the session was spent on slow speech training. The homework was for the parents to deliberately slow their rate of speech once a day when talking to a stranger or someone outside the family.

*Ninth Session*: Due to the Christmas holidays and other schedule problems, this session occurred three months after the eighth session. David came with the parents for slow speech training. The mother reported that overall, things had been "pretty manageable" since the last meeting. David's speech had been "good," which made her feel "good." They reported they had not been having talk times. It was suggested they start again since they were for the parents, not the child.

The therapy session was devoted to all three practicing slow speech. The importance of modeling slow speech rather than telling the child to slow down was stressed. Several role plays were conducted in which this was practiced. David agreed to help mom and dad talk slower!

Homework was one talk time for mother and one for father, but using slow speech. David was to monitor.

*Tenth Session*: The homework went well. The father needed to work on slowing speech movements. David did slow speech well. The father reported that he enjoyed the talk times and that he noticed that David slowed down sometimes by himself. Mother used slow speech " . . . a lot. There was one time this week when he was excited and I started talking slower and he said, 'Oh yeah' and slowed his speech also. I didn't have to say a word."

Both parents noticed that the first week when they were using slow speech that David would mouth the words with them.

The homework sheet revealed the following report from the mother:

I like this exercise and I feel less self-conscious around David when I'm trying to talk slower. To set the pace at this level really seemed to relax me and David both. I like to help David by example more than telling him because I don't feel like I'm nagging or putting pressure on him. He seems quite receptive to this approach, so I'm real happy about it. I enjoy this because speaking slower encourages me not to talk too much and dominate. After we finish I find myself still talking slower. It's a very positive time for us.

The father said,

I felt a lot more comfortable doing this than I did when I was first trying to learn. I found myself talking slower even after talk time was over.

Both parents reported that David was glad to resume the talk times and becomes excited when it was time for them.

*Eleventh Session*: The parents reported that David's speech was "okay and doing well." "David picks up quick. When we talk slower, he talks slower." Dad reported that David's speech was not a problem anymore but their daughter was beginning to have some fluency difficulty but they felt they knew how to handle it.

Two months after the last session, the father called to ask about the daughter's speech. When asked how David's speech was progressing, the response was, "We can write off, or we have written off, David's stuttering problem."

A letter was received from the mother approximately one year from the last session:

Things are going well here with the usual activities. David is six now and very fluent most of the time. Nancy, almost three and a half, is having some trouble with fluency. At times it's very noticeable, other times not so apparent. Believe it or not, it really doesn't bother me as much any more! We're using problem solving techniques to address a variety of situations— some just between my husband and me, others involving one or both kids. It's been a real help in working out a lot of stuff, serious or minor. Hope to hear from you soon!

*Mother's Reflection*: When Nancy started having trouble I think I regressed a bit. Since both of my children exhibited this I began to doubt if it wasn't really me or our family. I thought others probably wondered that, too (like my mother). With Nancy I felt more irritation, more exasperations, partly because I had been dealing with speech stuff for so long, and partly because hers was more severe than David's. Once when I called you desperate for you to just see her and see how bad it was (to feel sorry for me, probably) and you wouldn't and said you just wanted to see me, I could have wrung your neck. I thought you believed I was the problem. I think it was at that appointment that you told me both of your sons went through a time of dysfluency, and you're a speech pathologist. I felt better then and I decided to try again to believe it wasn't my fault. It took a lot of encouragement. I remember during that time you said something to me that I think is significant and was to me then. You told me to quit exaggerating about her speech difficulties (like, she does it a million times a day). It was a good thing to point out, and I've remembered it when I have a tendency to catastrophize.

That topic that bring me to another thing I wanted to menton because it was significant during our therapy. It has to do with you. At first when I had your number to call I was too upset, so much at a loss from what everyone was telling me to do or not to do, I was so nervous to call. I didn't know what to do or where to turn and all I had was some unknown university's professor's number. I remember very clearly when I first talked to you, Dick, how friendly you were, how easy you were to talk to. You made it much easier for me to follow through with the whole thing. I knew we were going to be evaluated and I expected to be targeted with blame for the stuttering. Had you been more reserved and formal or distant, I would have struggled a lot more, I know. And, since you were willing to discuss issues of our lives beyond speech, as one experienced parent to two fairly inexperienced parents, I felt you were interested in us as people, not case studies. And, when we got into more complicated, painful areas, I could face them more confidently within a supportive atmosphere. I guess there's no place to include this sort of feedback in your report, but it is a significant part of our therapy. The clinician must maintain an objective, professional stance to be helpful, but good "bedside manner" goes a long way. So, thank you.

The following comment made by the mother in her reflections represents better than anything I could have said about the necessity of working with the entire family.

*Mother's Reflections*: One more thing about David and Nancy. The other day David was listening to Nancy who was struggling a lot to get something out. As she struggled he frowned and inched closer to her, looking intently in her face. When it was time for his response, he very deliberately, but without explanation, began to use slow speech in a very comforting tone. He was so serious, so intent, and she began talking slower. You would have been proud.